Leader's / Catechist's Manual

Catholicism and Ethics

Rev. Edward J. Hayes
Rev. Msgr. Paul J. Hayes
Dorothy Ellen Kelly, R.N.
and James J. Drummey

"The Ad Hoc Committee to Oversee the Use of the Catechism, National Conference of Catholic Bishops, has found the doctrinal content of this teacher manual to be in conformity with the Catechism of the Catholic Church.*"*

C.R. Publications Inc.
345 Prospect Street
Norwood, Massachusetts 02062

NIHIL OBSTAT
Msgr. William E. Maguire
Censor Librorum

IMPRIMATUR
+ Most Reverend John M. Smith
Bishop of Trenton
October 15, 1999

The Nihil Obstat and Imprimatur are official declarations that a book or pamphlet is free of doctrinal or moral error. No implication is contained therein that those who have granted the Nihil Obstat or Imprimatur agree with the contents, opinions, or statements expressed.

Cover design by Jeff Giniewicz
Printed in the United States of America
ISBN 0-9649087-8-6

Contents

How to Get the Most Out of This Book 5

1. The Nature and Basis of Ethics 15

2. Contrary Moral Theories 22

3. The Morality of Human Acts 27

4. Conditions Affecting Morality 31

5. Natural Law and God's Law 36

6. Forming a Right Conscience 42

7. Twofold or Double Effect 46

8. Ordinary vs. Extraordinary Means 50

9. Moral Guides and Maxims 55

10. Cooperation in Evil 58

11. Opposition to Contraception 62

12. Paul VI and Humanae Vitae 68

13. John Paul II and the Catechism 72

14. Contraception vs. NFP 77

15. Manipulating Human Life 82

16. The Destruction of Life 87

17. Abortion Penalties and Compassion 93

18. Euthanasia and Assisted Suicide 98

19. Mutilation and Sterilization 102

20. Artificial Nutrition and Hydration 105

21. Hypnosis, Drugs and AIDS 109

22. Spiritual Help for the Suffering 113

How to Get the Most Out of This Book

The purpose of *Catholicism and Ethics* is to apply basic Catholic moral and ethical principles to developments in the fast-changing fields of science, biology, genetics, and bioethics. Because many of these developments literally involve life-and-death decisions, *Catholicism and Ethics* will be helpful to a wide audience—from high school students to senior citizens. It is a valuable handbook for individuals and families and an excellent text for adult education or informal study groups; for college, university, and nursing students; and for those in Catholic high schools or parish religious education programs.

The book is an essential resource for Catholics because it shows how the moral and ethical principles discussed, which are taken from Scripture, the natural law, and the Magisterium or teaching office of the Catholic Church, will always be pertinent and applicable to the latest discoveries in the fields of science and medicine.

The book not only lends itself to a one-semester or one-year course, but it can also be broken down into mini-courses. Some examples:

1. A course on ethics and morality, the morality of human acts, and law and conscience (chapters 1-3 of the text).

2. A course on the double effect, moral guides and maxims, and the morality of cooperation (chapters 4-6 of the text).

3. A course on the origins of life — contraception, cloning, "test-tube" babies, and artificial insemination (chapter 7 of the text).

4. A course on the taking of life — abortion, euthanasia, and advance medical directives (chapter 8 of the text).

5. A course on the preservation of life, covering sterilization, artificial nutrition and hydration, and tissue and organ
transplants (chapter 9 of the text).

There are other possibilities and variations as well, depending on what you want to offer or what religious voids need
to be filled. Many parishes are scheduling adult education
programs during the year and offering courses one night a week
for five or six weeks. A series of this type can be very successful, especially during Advent or Lent, and this volume, or its
companion texts, *Catholicism and Reason*, *Catholicism and
Life*, and *Catholicism and Society*, would be very appropriate
for such a series.

But whatever material and format you choose, few books
lend themselves better to discussion of current and controversial issues than *Catholicism and Ethics*. The text will give
Catholics the ammunition they need to do battle with those
who are challenging and violating basic ethical and moral principles. Armed with this information, clergy and laity will then
be able to advance the cause of human rights for all persons
from conception until their natural end.

Specific suggestions for stimulating interest and initiat-
ing discussion can be found under the individual lessons. (Because of the length of the chapters in the text, this manual is
arranged by lessons.) These suggestions, of course, are not all-
encompassing, but they should provide some practical ideas
for the catechist or group leader. The lessons contain plenty
of information for classes of forty-five to sixty minutes, but
they need not be confined to one class; in some cases, the catechist or teacher may want to spend more time on a subject,
for example, studying in detail Pope Paul's *Humanae Vitae* or
Pope John Paul's *Evangelium Vitae*.

It will be up to the individual catechist to decide how much
time should be spent on each lesson and how the time should
be divided between lecture and discussion. Some groups are
more responsive than others and make the teacher's job easier.
Whatever the situation, no catechist should have difficulty
preparing an interesting and effective class.

Generally speaking, the suggestions for presenting the

material will be helpful whether you are teaching high schoolers, college-age students, or adults, although there are certain topics, questions, and projects that will be more appropriate for one age group than another. The catechist will have to be the judge of that.

In addition to the specific tips on teaching from *Catholicism and Ethics*, the following general comments — not necessarily in the order of their importance — may be helpful.

1. *Read the entire book and catechist's manual before you begin teaching.* Not only should you do this to familiarize yourself with the entire course, but it will be useful if you are questioned about a matter that will be covered later in the course. You could then answer the question briefly, note that it will be taken up in more detail at another time, and refer the questioner to the appropriate chapter for additional information.

2. *State your goals at the beginning of each class.* Tell the students what you expect to cover and what is expected of them. Be yourself, be in charge, keep things simple and concrete (it is not easy to grasp abstract concepts), give clear directions, and have a sense of humor. Use your lesson plan as a road map with different routes. Don't be afraid to switch directions and even to take up something new to keep the attention of the class. Start out with some life experience or event in the news that is familiar to the students, then present the doctrine or message you want to convey in that particular class, and finally attempt to elicit some faith response from them.

Try to vary your lessons with different methods and activities. Use some lecture, some dialogue, some student presentations, some problem-solving, some projects, and even some games (adapt "Wheel of Fortune" or "Jeopardy" or "Family Feud" or "Hangman" to the information to be covered). Ask the students to rate things in the order of their importance (conditions that affect morality, the Ten Commandments, moral guides and maxims, nine ways of cooperating in sin, reasons why euthanasia is wrong, the AA's twelve steps, etc.) to stimulate discussion. Ask them their top five choices of ethical and moral problems facing society today.

3. *Although the material in* Catholicism and Ethics *can be presented effectively in lecture form, the ideal way to develop it is through discussion.* Students are more likely to remember things if they have had a chance to talk about them, ask questions, and even figure out some of the answers themselves. By discussion, it should be made clear, we do not mean an aimless stream of consciousness where everybody's opinion is equally valid and where nothing is resolved. We mean rather an atmosphere where the teacher teaches and the student learns; where questions, comments, and dialogue are encouraged under the guidance and direction of the catechist; where facts are stated by the catechist if the students do not come up with them; and where the catechist summarizes the matter discussed at the end of the class, answering all questions as well as possible and trying to resolve all doubts.

4. *Instead of merely stating the points to be covered, catechists should seek to draw the information out of the students.* Catechists should be constantly asking questions, making the students think, and inviting them to participate in the class. When you first ask a question, do not direct it to a particular student lest the others in the class assume that they are safe and can stop paying attention. Ask the question first of the entire class and then, if no one volunteers an answer, direct it to a particular person. Do not allow a few students to monopolize the discussion. Try to involve everyone, especially those who seem not to be paying attention. Be careful not to embarrass the shy or reticent student, but try to bring them out of their shell. When students ask what you think about some matter, turn the question back to them and ask, "What do you think?" Your goal is to keep all the students involved.

5. *Keep the class interesting and current through the use of stories, anecdotes, and up-to-date items related to the subject matter.* Storytelling is an effective way to make a point, as our Lord proved with his use of parables. Have the students bring into class pertinent items from newspapers and magazines, especially those critical of the Church's stand, so you can correct the misinformation. Get them in the habit of watching for these things and you will have a successful class.

Remember, however, that media accounts of religious issues are often slanted, out of context, misleading, or just plain wrong. Insist that authentic documents, not some reporter's biased view of a Church teaching, be used to form the basis of any valid discussion.

6. *Define all terms, even if it seems unnecessary.* You should not assume that any medical or ethical or religious term is understood correctly, so ask the students what it means and then spell out the definition for them. Unless the students understand exactly what you are talking about, you will either lose them or misinform them. A Catholic dictionary or encyclopedia, or the glossary section of the *Catholic Almanac*, will be most helpful in providing definitions. As the *General Directory for Catechesis* says, "Secure possession of the language of the faith is an indispensable condition for living that same faith" (n. 154).

And don't be afraid to have the students memorize definitions, the words of Jesus, important Bible passages, doctrinal ideas, liturgical formulas, and the commonly known prayers of our Catholic tradition, such as the Apostles' Creed, Our Father, Hail Mary, and so forth. Memorization of such things, Pope John Paul said, "far from being opposed to the dignity of young Christians, or constituting an obstacle to personal dialogue with the Lord, is a real need. . . . We must be realists. The blossoms, if we may call them that, of faith and piety do not grow in the desert places of a memory-less catechesis" (*On Catechesis in Our Time*, n. 55).

7. *Use the chalkboard and other visual aids as much as possible.* The old saying that one picture is worth a thousand words is still true. Children remember about 10 percent of what they hear, 50 percent of what they see and hear, and 90 percent of what they see, hear, and do. You can talk about abortion and its horrors for hours and not convince anyone that it is evil, but one video showing the beautiful developing child at 12 weeks, or the crushed and bloody remains of an aborted baby, can make a profound impression.

Not all issues can be as graphically portrayed as abortion,

but any maps, slides, pictures, audio and video cassettes, tape recordings, compact discs, etc., that can be used to illustrate a point will add immeasurably to your class. "In every well-planned catechesis," says the *General Directory for Catechesis*, "such aids cannot be absent" (n. 160). Even simply writing things on the board will also make a difference in getting the material across to the students. Or holding up flash cards that say AGREE or DISAGREE after you make a statement. Do not neglect any tool that will make your class more informative and interesting.

8. *Review what you have covered previously.* It is a good idea to use the beginning of each class to summarize, or have the students summarize, what has been covered thus far, particularly in the previous class. In this way, you will know what is getting across and what needs to be repeated. If time permits, you could give brief quizzes at the beginning of class to prepare the ground for the next phase of the course. Quizzes and tests are important, even in once-a-week religion classes, if we expect the students to take the subject seriously.

9. *State the position of the Church clearly and unequivocally.* This is most important since many Catholics are confused today on where their Church stands. Your job is not to give your own opinion or that of some popular theologian, but rather the definitive teaching of the infallible Church of Christ. "Catechists for their part," Pope John Paul said, "must have the wisdom to pick from the field of theological research those points that can provide light for their own reflection and their teaching, drawing, like the theologians, from the true sources, in the light of the magisterium. They must refuse to trouble the minds of the children and young people, at this stage of their catechesis, with outlandish theories, useless questions, and unproductive discussions, things that St. Paul often condemned in his pastoral letters" (*On Catechesis in Our Time*, n. 61).

This adherence to the truth is a solemn responsibility. Make sure that the class always knows what the Church's teaching is and the reason for that teaching. If you do not know the answer to a question, do not try to fool the students. Tell them that you will find the answer—and then do so. Do not get bogged down in certain areas, and do not worry if you cannot completely convince all your students about the merits of a specific teaching. Do your best to present the view of the Church and then leave it to the Holy Spirit to enlighten the minds of your listeners.

10. *Assign projects and homework so as to involve the class more deeply in the course.* This course offers a good opportunity to encourage familiarity with Church and papal documents. There are also numerous works listed at the end of each lesson that the students should be assigned to consult and report on to the class. Have one or two students give a five-minute talk each class. This will prepare them to talk about moral and ethical principles just as freely and intelligently as they talk about sports or movies or music.

Get them to write letters every month, to lawmakers, newspapers, etc., addressing important issues, and urge them to recruit others — students, relatives, friends — in this apostolate.

Speaking of references, there are certain books that are invaluable to catechists and should be a part of their own library. These include a Bible, a Catholic dictionary, a one-volume Catholic encyclopedia, a Catholic almanac, the *Catechism of the Catholic Church*, the documents of Vatican II, a history of the Catholic Church, a life of Christ, a dictionary of the saints, a good question-and-answer book like *Catholic Replies*, the *General Directory for Catechesis*, and, for this volume, such pertinent papal documents as Pope Pius XII's *Casti Connubii*, Pope Paul's *Humanae Vitae*, and Pope John Paul's *Familiaris Consortio* and *Evangelium Vitae*.

11. *Encourage daily prayer, frequent reception of the Sacraments, and the performance of good works.* Remind the students often about the importance of daily prayer, at least weekly Mass and Communion, and frequent Confession. Urge them to carry out works of charity, either individually or collectively. Begin and end each class with a prayer, inviting the students to suggest prayers and to lead the class in saying them. A decade of the rosary is a good way to start a class period. The teacher can be an actual grace for the students by inspiring

them to do good and avoid evil and always to remain close to Jesus and his Church. Catechists who demonstrate a sincere interest in the well-being of their students, who pray with them and for them, who are available to them after class for any help or advice they may need can have a positive and long-lasting influence on the young people entrusted to them.

As the *General Directory for Catechesis* reminds us: "No methodology, no matter how well tested, can dispense with the person of the catechist in every phase of the catechetical process. The charism given to him by the Spirit, a solid spirituality and transparent witness of life, constitutes the soul of every method. Only his own human and Christian qualities guarantee a good use of texts and other work instruments" (n. 156).

12. *For high school religion teachers, acquaint the parents of your students with the course.* There are three things necessary for a successful CCD or religious education program—good books, good teachers, and interested parents. We have provided the first requirement and contributed to the second. The third is up to you. Contact all the parents at the beginning of the year, invite them to a meeting to explain the course to them, urge them to send their children to class faithfully, and invite them to visit the classroom or to contact you if they have any questions or suggestions. Some students will tell parents that they don't want to go to class because "we're not learning anything." Parents who know what is being taught to their children will not be swayed by that argument.

13. *It is important for the catechist to realize that the work of helping others to grow and mature in the Christian life is primarily the work of the Holy Spirit.* The catechist, Pope John Paul said, "must be very much aware of acting as a living, pliant instrument of the Holy Spirit. To invoke this Spirit constantly, to be in communion with him, to endeavor to know his authentic inspirations must be the attitude of the teaching Church and of every catechist" (*On Catechesis in Our Time*, n. 72)

"The effectiveness of catechists is and always will be a gift of God, through the operation of the Spirit of the Father and the Son," says the *General Directory for Catechesis.* "St. Paul, in his letter to the Corinthians, confirms this total dependence on the intervention of God when he writes: 'I planted, Apollos watered, but God gave the growth. So neither he who plants nor he who waters is anything, but only God who gives the growth' (1 Corinthians 3:6-7). Neither catechesis nor evangelization is possible without the action of God working through his Spirit. In catechetical praxis, neither the most advanced pedagogical techniques nor the most talented catechist can ever replace the silent and unseen action of the Holy Spirit" (n. 288).

Finally, catechists must be fully committed to show "who Jesus Christ is, his life and ministry, and to present the Christian faith as the following of his person." They must base their catechesis "constantly on the Gospels, which are the heart of all the Scriptures because they are our principal source for the life and teaching of the Incarnate Word, our Savior" (*General Directory for Catechesis,* n. 41).

The fundamental tasks of catechesis, says the *General Directory,* include promoting knowledge of the faith, celebrating the presence of Jesus in the Sacraments and especially in the Eucharist, presenting the moral code of the Master as contained in the Ten Commandments and the Sermon on the Mount, and encouraging people to learn to pray with Jesus "with the same sentiments with which he turned to the Father: adoration, praise, thanksgiving, filial confidence, supplication, and awe for his glory."

The *Directory* says that "all of these sentiments are reflected in the Our Father, the prayer which Jesus taught his disciples and which is the model of all Christian prayer. The handing on of the Our Father is a summary of the entire Gospel and is therefore a true act of catechesis" (n. 85).

Author's Note: We remind the catechist or group leader again that many of the discussion points and projects in this manual are geared to high school students. However, since the text will also be used in colleges, nursing schools, and adult discussion groups, the instructor in those classes should feel free to adapt the suggestions to the particular audience that is using the text.

The Nature and Basis of Ethics

Purpose: The purpose of this lesson is to show how the science of ethics can guide our judgment about the morality of human acts.

Tips for Teachers: The first part of this class will necessarily have to be taken up with seating arrangements, attendance, and rules for classroom conduct. It will be important for the catechist of high school students to state clearly what is expected of the teenagers. The atmosphere created in the first class can set the tone for the year. Catechists should express their policies and expectations clearly and firmly so as to prevent misunderstandings and problems from arising later on.

One obvious and essential rule is that only one person speaks at a time, either the catechist or one of the students who has been properly recognized. A courteous and respectful atmosphere is the only setting in which religion or any other subject can be effectively presented by the catechist and completely understood by the students.

The catechist should also mention such things as homework assignments, quizzes, tests, and special projects—in other words, the various techniques and methods that will be used to develop the subject matter, impart knowledge to the students, and encourage them to practice their Faith.

Once the preliminaries are over, the remainder of the class should be spent discussing the general nature and purpose of the course, with emphasis on some of the more interesting and challenging subjects to be covered—abortion, AIDS, artificial insemination, artificial nutrition and hydration, cloning, contraception, cooperation in evil, drug addiction, euthanasia, extraordinary vs. ordinary means, fertility tests, hypnosis, mutilation of the body, narcotics to the dying, Natural Family Planning, organ donations, physician-assisted suicide, surrogate motherhood, "test tube" babies, and tissue transplants.

The catechist can then get into the material in lesson 1, perhaps by putting the terms "Love of God" and "Love of Neighbor" on the board at the head of two columns and then asking for examples that would fit under each heading. For instance, love of God would certainly include respect for all life which comes from the Creator, and love of neighbor would rule out killing an innocent person by abortion or euthanasia. These and other examples can set the stage for many of the issues to be discussed in future classes.

The basic points to be covered in this lesson are the definition of ethics, its relation to moral theology, and the truths upon which ethics is based. The catechist or group leader could break down the definition of ethics on page 13 of the text. Point out that it is a science, that is, it deals with a body of facts and truths. It is, however, a *natural* science in that it is not based on the law of God, which would make it supernatural, but rather on the power of human reason.

It is not a *physical* science or something that is studied just for the sake of study, but rather a *practical* science since its principles can be applied to real-life actions and situations. It is also a *moral* science since it can help determine whether certain acts are good or bad. Ethics would be very important in a society where there was no God or Bible or church to help determine right from wrong.

Assign the students to read and then act out the parable of the Good Samaritan (Luke 10:25-37), perhaps even to put it in a modern setting, so as to illustrate that the science of ethics alone ought to prompt us to help those in need, regardless of whether we had ever heard of Jesus or his command that we must love our neighbor. Human reason and experience would be enough to compel us to act charitably toward a person who had been left for dead by the side of the road.

Next, the teacher or facilitator should discuss the sources (human reason and experience) from which ethical judgments are drawn, noting that neither the Bible nor the Church is cited since they are not really a source of ethics but rather a check on its conclusions. Spend time on each source, eliciting from the class examples of the use of one's reasoning process to arrive at a moral decision and examples of how experience, whether personal, contemporary, or historical, has influenced decisions they have made.

The connection can then be shown between ethics and moral theology, with reason and experience tending toward a natural end and divine revelation, as interpreted by the teaching office of the Church (the Magisterium), encompassing a supernatural end. Thus, a person with good ethics can still have bad morals if his reasoning and experience are based on what contemporary society thinks rather than on what God thinks. Ask the class for examples of such a person.

The 14 truths listed on page 15 could also serve almost as a whole lesson in themselves. Ask the students to rate them in the order of importance. If you want to spend some time on them, you could talk, for instance, about Pontius Pilate's famous question to Jesus, "Truth! What does that mean?" (John 18:38), or about Jesus' statement that "I am the truth" (John 14:6), or about the existence of God (see chapter 2 of *Catholicism and Reason*, a companion volume in this series, for ways of reasoning to the existence of God), or the justice of God that includes heaven and hell, or the immortality of the soul, or our free will that enables us to choose God or to reject him.

The books by Fr. John Hardon, Peter Kreeft, and Frank Sheed that are listed under references, as well as the pertinent sections in the *Catechism of the Catholic Church*, would be helpful in talking about the soul and free will.

Topics for Discussion:

1. What are some areas of society where sound ethical principles are sorely needed?

2. How can two people with the same education, background, and training come to opposite conclusions about such issues as abortion and euthanasia?

3. Can a person with no knowledge of God or religion know right from wrong?

4. Give an example of using your reasoning powers to make a moral decision.

5. Give an example of where your personal experience might influence a future moral decision.

6. Give an example of where someone else's experience might influence your moral choices.

7. Why doesn't God force us to do good, instead of leaving us free to do bad things?

Some Questions and Answers:

1. How can we prove the existence of God through the use of human reason?

A. Two of the ways are from causality and intelligent design. While lengthier treatments of these arguments can be found in chapter two of *Catholicism and Reason*, here are brief explanations.

(1) Everything in the world must be caused by something or someone else. There is nothing that is the cause of itself. Using our own unaided reason, we can see that a long series of causes cannot go back in time indefinitely. You were caused by your parents, they by their parents, and so on, but there must have existed at the beginning something that was not caused by anything else, someone that began the whole series. That someone, that Uncaused Cause, we call God.

(2) If you look at the mechanism of a computer, you don't think that someone just threw a bunch of wires and chips and pieces of plastic and rubber into the air and, when they landed, a computer had been created. No, you marvel at the intricate workings of a computer and reason that it was put together by an intelligent designer.

By the same reasoning, when we look at the beauties of nature and the intricate workings of the universe, the design and order that allow astronauts to plan precise missions to the moon and back, we don't conclude that it all happened by chance or by coincidence. No, we reason that our marvelously constructed universe must have been planned by an intelligent designer, and that Intelligent Designer we call God.

If you believe in a computer-maker, you must logically believe in a Universe-Maker. You can find eighteen more arguments for the existence of God in chapter three of *Handbook of Christian Apologetics* by Peter Kreeft and Ronald Tacelli.

2. How can we be sure we have a soul and that it will live forever?

A. The soul is the principle of life, that which animates the body. If we see a person alive on Friday, but lying dead in a funeral home on Sunday, the most obvious difference is that the soul, the life principle, is absent from the dead person's body. The great Catholic writer Frank Sheed, in his book *Theology and Sanity*, discussed at some length the unity of body and soul in human beings. Herewith an excerpt from page 105 of that book:

> Man has a living body; therefore, there is some principle in him which makes his body to be alive. And whether a body be vegetable or lower animal or man, that principle in it which makes it living is what we call its soul. Man, then, has a soul; so has a dog, so has a cabbage: and man's soul does for his body what their souls do for theirs, makes it a living body.
>
> But whereas their souls are material, limited to matter, not producing any operation that goes beyond matter, man's soul is spirit. It does not only the things that souls do, but the things that spirits do. By intellect and will it knows and loves as spirits know and love: in its thinking it handles the abstract and the universal. Man, having a body and soul, is an animal; but he is a rational animal, for alone of the animals he has a soul which is a spirit.

Sheed compares the soul to the flame that sets a pot of water boiling and hissing. Just as the superior energy of the flame causes the movement of the water, so the energy of the soul moves and gives vitality to the body.

As for the immortality of the soul, here is Sheed on page 234 of his book:

> A point comes – suddenly if there is violence, or by slow wearing – when the body can no longer respond to the lifegiving energy of the soul. That, precisely, is death. The body, unvivified, falls away into its elements, not to be reunited with the soul, and once more whole and entire, till the end of the world. But the soul does not die with the body. Why should it? As a spirit, it does not depend for its life on the body: matter cannot give life to spirit. In the absence of the body, the soul cannot exercise its powers as the animator of a body, so that these must remain wrapt within it till the body rises again at the last day. But in its own nature as a spirit with intellect and will it lives on.

3. What does the Bible mean when it says that we are made in the image and likeness of God?

A. This means that God set out to make us in some way like himself and this resemblance is in our soul. Our soul is a spirit, having an intellect and a free will. Our ability to think and to choose and to love, to understand such abstract concepts as love, beauty, truth, wisdom, and justice, indicates something beyond our material body. Just as a painting reflects some of the characteristics of the artist, so our intellect and will reflect the image and likeness of our Creator.

Projects:

1. Act out the parable of the Good Samaritan in a modern-day situation.

2. Interview a family member or friend about an experience that caused them to make an important moral decision.

3. Write to an elected official (United States Senator or Congressman, state or local representative) and ask why he or she voted for or against legislation dealing with abortion, euthanasia, or physician-assisted suicide.

4. Write a letter to the local newspaper or radio or television station and ask for a story on the need for sound ethical principles in public life.

References:

Catechism of the Catholic Church
Catholic Almanac
Catholic Encyclopedia. Edited by Fr. Peter M.J. Stravinskas
Drummey, James J. Catholic Replies
Duggan, G.H., S.M. Beyond Reasonable Doubt
Encyclopedia of Catholic Doctrine. Edited by Russell Shaw
Flannery, Austin, O.P. Vatican Council II: The Conciliar
        and Post Conciliar Documents
Grisez, Germain. Christian Moral Principles
_____. Difficult Moral Questions
_____. Living a Christian Life
Hardon, John A., S.J. The Catholic Catechism
_____. Modern Catholic Dictionary
_____. The Question and Answer Catholic Catechism

Hayes, Edward J., Hayes, Paul J. and Drummey, James J.
    Catholicism and Life
    _____. *Catholicism and Reason*
    _____. *Catholicism and Society*
John Paul II, Pope. *Evangelium Vitae* ("The Gospel of Life")
    _____. *Veritatis Splendor* ("The Splendor of Truth")
Kreeft, Peter, and Tacelli, Ronald K. *Handbook of Christian
    Apologetics*
Sheed, Frank. *Theology and Sanity*
    _____. *Theology for Beginners*
Wuerl, Donald, Lawler, Thomas and Lawler, Ronald. *The
    Catholic Catechism*
    _____. *The Teaching of Christ*

Lesson 2 (pp. 16-20)

Contrary Moral Theories

Purpose: The purpose of this lesson is to show how divine revelation (the Bible and Sacred Tradition) and the teaching office of the Catholic Church help us to make good moral decisions and to avoid contrary theories that attempt to make evil actions appear to be good.

Tips for Teachers: This lesson offers an opportunity to emphasize the importance of divine revelation and the teaching office of the Church when seeking confirmation of the moral choices we have made through the application of ethical principles. The catechist or group leader could refer to chapters 12 and 13 of *Catholicism and Reason* for more information on the place of Scripture and Tradition in our lives and the authority of the Church that Jesus left us to interpret these twin sources of God's will for everyone.

Stress the necessity of having a living authority to tell us what the Bible and Tradition mean. Leaving this interpretation up to individuals to make has led to a multiplicity of churches and denominations, all holding contradictory and competing views, as well as a variety of moral theories about how we determine right from wrong. Private interpretation makes everyone his own pope, while faithful Catholics follow the guidance of only one Pope.

This would be a good time to review with the class some of the key passages in the Bible which demonstrate that Jesus gave the Church and the Pope the authority to speak in his name. Some Bible passages that should be looked at include Matthew 16:18-19, Luke 22:31-32, John 14:16-17, John 21:15-17, and 1 Timothy 3:15.

Since the Catholic Church was established by Christ to help us get to heaven, she is very concerned about ethical and moral principles, especially in the medical field. Note that God is not only the Author of all life, but also the Author of all the physical and moral laws in the universe. Thus, there can be no conflict between moral and scientific principles since they stem from the same divine source. Emphasize the statement from Pope Pius XII that no matter how important science and culture are, love of God and devotion to his service must come first in our lives.

Against the clear teachings of God and the Church, however, contrary theories of morality are always being advanced. There are the simple examples of conventional wisdom, such as "Everyone is doing it," or "If it's legal, it must be moral," or "If it relieves someone's burden or suffering, we should go ahead and do it,"and so forth.

Then there are the more complicated theories, such as basing one's moral choices on the situation (situation ethics), or on the consequences of the action (consequentialism), or on how we feel about something (subjectivism). Pope John Paul's encyclical on "The Splendor of Truth" (*Veritatis Splendor*), as well as the information under "Some Questions and Answers," will help to show the falsity of these dangerous theories.

Topics for Discussion:

1. How would you answer Mark, who says, "I don't need the Church to tell me what to do. I can make up my own mind."

2. Is one person's moral view as good as another's?

3. What did Jesus mean when he said to Peter, "Whatever you declare bound on earth shall be bound in heaven"?

4. How would you respond to the statement, "Everybody's doing it, so why shouldn't I?" [See Exodus 23:2, where God tells Moses: "Neither shall you allege the example of the many as an excuse for doing wrong."]

5. What are some results of basing moral decisions on feelings instead of on ethical principles?

6. List five actions that are always and everywhere wrong.

Some Questions and Answers:

1. The Bible was written thousands of years ago. How can it have any relevance for us today?

A. Human nature does not change and people face the same moral decisions and dilemmas today as our ancestors did. Note the statement above where God told Moses to warn the people not to attempt to justify a course of action just because other people are doing it. Or think of Adam and Eve's reaction when God asked them why they had disobeyed him by eating the forbidden fruit. Did they admit their sinfulness and take responsibility for their actions? Not at all. Adam blamed Eve for his transgression, and Eve blamed the serpent (Genesis 3:12-13).

There are many examples, good and bad, of men and women in millennia gone by acting just as humans act today. For instance, we have Cain killing his brother Abel out of jealousy, Abraham unhesitatingly putting his faith in God, Joseph recognizing the working of God's plan in his life, King David ordering a soldier put in harm's way so that he could have the soldier's wife, Judith helping to save her people by slaying the evil Holofernes, and the martyrdom in Maccabeean times of a mother and her seven sons rather than eat pork in violation of God's law.

The same litany of moral and immoral actions, courageous and cowardly human conduct also continues through the New Testament as exemplified by the courage of John the Baptist, the faithfulness of the Virgin Mary, the betrayal of Judas, the cowardice of Pontius Pilate, the denial of St. Peter, the bravery of St. Paul, and so forth.

The Bible will always be relevant because the people and events described in Scripture are so typical of people and events in our own time.

2. What is the theory of situation ethics, and where did it originate?

A. This theory was popularized by the late Joseph Fletcher in a book entitled *Situation Ethics: The New Morality*. The theory denies any absolute standards of morality and says that the morality of each action is to be determined by the particular situation or circumstances surrounding the action. According to Fletcher, any act, including lying, premarital sex, abortion, adultery, and even murder could be morally right because "whatever is the most loving thing in the situation is the right and good thing. It is not excusably evil, it is positively good."

Any theory that can call these evils good is far removed from the teachings of Christ and his Church and must be firmly opposed.

3. What is the theory of subjectivism and what is wrong with it?

A. Subjectivism holds that one's individual feelings, rather than objective moral law, determine right from wrong. It is rooted in a pride which says that the individual is God and that the only norm of conduct is the individual's personal and subjective choice. You can see the dangers of each person setting his or her own moral code in the following examples:

> "I know the speed limit is 65, but I'm such a good driver I can go 85." "I know the Bible says homosexual behavior is wrong, but I feel that it's okay for two people who really love each other." "I know that some people think abortion is wrong, but having a baby now would ruin my college career." "I can't stand to see my grandmother suffer any longer, so I'm going to ask the doctor to end her life."

St. Paul warned against this kind of thinking in his Second Letter to Timothy (4:2-4):

> I charge you to preach the word, to stay with this task whether convenient or inconvenient — correcting, reproving, appealing — constantly teaching and never losing patience. For the time will come when people will not tolerate sound doctrine, but, following their own desires, will surround themselves with teachers who tickle their ears. They will stop listening to the truth and will wander off to fables.

Projects:

1. Make a poster of the chart on page 18 of the text.

2. Make a chart listing the key Gospel references to the authority of the Pope and the Church.

3. Act out Jesus' dialogue with Pontius Pilate (John 18:28-19:16) and discuss what Pilate should have done.

4. Make a poster listing those actions mentioned in "The Splendor of Truth" that are always and everywhere wrong (cf. sections 80, 81, and 100).

5. Volunteer to teach religion to young children.

References:

Catechism of the Catholic Church
Catholic Almanac
Catholic Encyclopedia. Edited by Fr. Peter M.J. Stravinskas
Drummey, James J. *Catholic Replies*
Duggan, G.H., S.M. *Beyond Reasonable Doubt*
Encyclopedia of Catholic Doctrine. Edited by Russell Shaw
Flannery, Austin, O.P. *Vatican Council II: The Conciliar
    and Post Conciliar Documents*
Grisez, Germain. *Christian Moral Principles*
_____. *Difficult Moral Questions*
_____. *Living a Christian Life*
Hardon, John A., S.J. *The Catholic Catechism*
_____. *Modern Catholic Dictionary*
_____. *The Question and Answer Catholic Catechism*
Hayes, Edward J., Hayes, Paul J. and Drummey, James J.
    Catholicism and Life
_____. *Catholicism and Reason*
_____. *Catholicism and Society*
John Paul II, Pope. *Evangelium Vitae* ("The Gospel of Life")
_____. *Veritatis Splendor* ("The Splendor of Truth")
Kreeft, Peter, and Tacelli, Ronald K. *Handbook of Christian
    Apologetics*
May, William E. *An Introduction to Moral Theology*
Sheed, Frank. *Theology and Sanity*
_____. *Theology for Beginners*
Wuerl, Donald, Lawler, Thomas and Lawler, Ronald. *The
    Catholic Catechism*
_____. *The Teaching of Christ*

The Morality of Human Acts

Purpose: The purpose of this lesson is to show that every human act derives its morality from three elements: the act itself, the purpose of the act, and the circumstances surrounding the act, and that all three must be good for the act to be moral.

Tips for Teachers: This class could be started by asking what factors determine whether an action is right or wrong. If the students already know the three important elements in deciding morality, then initiate a detailed discussion of each of them, with examples to illustrate them. Sections 71-83 of "The Splendor of Truth" and sections 1749-1761 of the *Catechism of the Catholic Church* will be helpful here.

Emphasize that, as Pope John Paul said, the act itself is the most important element because it establishes whether the act is capable of being ordered to the good. Some acts are always good (ask for examples), some are always evil (ask for examples), and some are neutral and depend for their morality on intention and circumstances (ask for examples).

The second element is the reason why the act is performed, i.e., the intention of the one performing the act. This intention or purpose will not always change the morality of the act itself because some acts (ask for examples) are wrong by their nature, and no good intention can make right that which is intrinsically wrong.

The third element, the circumstances surrounding the act, can affect the morality of the act, making it more evil (setting a fire at night) or making the person less guilty (being forced to drive a getaway car or getting drunk because someone spiked your drink).

Having covered each of the three elements, the catechist or group leader can then carefully review the five principles on pages 26-27 and discuss the various examples. Ask the class to come up with additional examples. Point No. 5 is especially important because all three elements must be good, or at least neutral, for the act to be good. Just as one polluted stream will contaminate a whole pond, so one bad element will render the act immoral.

You can then jump ahead a few pages and spend some time on occasions of sin (pages 38-40) as part of this lesson. This is pertinent since occasions of sin are outside circumstances, either persons, places, or things, that can induce a person to sin. Ask the students to give examples of how many sins could be avoided if we stayed away from occasions of sin.

Use the chart on page 39 to show the difference between proximate and remote occasions of sin and those that are voluntary and necessary. Suggest or ask for steps that we can take to stay away from occasions of sin.

Topics for Discussion:

1. What elements go into determining whether an act is moral or immoral?
2. Can a good intention make an evil act good?
3. Why is the nature of the act, i.e., the act itself, so important in deciding the morality of the act?
4. Can you think of a person who might lead you to sin?
5. Can you think of a place that might lead you to sin?
6. Can you think of a thing that might lead you to sin?
7. What specifically can you do to avoid occasions of sin?

Some Questions and Answers:

1. Where can I find a list of actions that are always and everywhere wrong?
A. See sections 80, 81, and 100 of "The Splendor of Truth," where Pope John Paul compiles such a list from the Bible and from the documents of the Second Vatican Council. You can also look up the Bible references to the four sins that cry to heaven for God's vengeance. They are willful murder (Genesis 4:10), sodomy or homosexual acts (Genesis 18:20, 19:5-7), oppression of the poor (Exodus 2:23), and defrauding laborers of their wages (James 5:4).

These are not necessarily the four *worst* sins that a person can commit, but they have been singled out in Scripture because the cries of their victims were heard by God, and he came to their assistance.

2. Will people who commit these and other terrible sins automatically go to hell?
A. No, not if they are truly sorry for their sins. There is no sin that God will not forgive, except the sin of final impenitence. "Every sin, every blasphemy, will be forgiven men," said Jesus, "but blasphemy against the Spirit will not be forgiven" (Matthew 12:31). This refers to final impenitence, which is the obstinate rejection of God's mercy and forgiveness, even at the moment of death. Such a person does not even seek pardon, but completely and finally rejects the assistance the Holy Spirit offers to turn the person away from evil and back to God.

"This is a state of spiritual ruin," said Pope John Paul in his encyclical "On the Holy Spirit in the Life of the Church" (*Dominum et Vivificantem*) "because blasphemy against the Holy Spirit does not allow one to escape from one's self-imposed imprisonment and open oneself to the divine sources of the purification of consciences and of the remission of sins" (n. 46).

Projects:

1. Read and summarize orally or in writing the important points in sections 71-83 of "The Splendor of Truth."

2. Read and summarize orally or in writing the important points in sections 1749-1761 of the *Catechism of the Catholic Church*.

3. Clip from the daily newspaper one story about an immoral act and apply the three elements of morality to it.

4. Recall an immoral act from a television show or a movie and apply the three elements of morality to it.

5. Make a large poster of the chart on page 39.

References:

Catechism of the Catholic Church
Catholic Almanac
Catholic Encyclopedia. Edited by Fr. Peter M.J. Stravinskas

Drummey, James J. *Catholic Replies*
Encyclopedia of Catholic Doctrine. Edited by Russell Shaw
Flannery, Austin, O.P. *Vatican Council II: The Conciliar and Post Conciliar Documents*
Grisez, Germain. *Christian Moral Principles*
_____. *Difficult Moral Questions*
_____. *Living a Christian Life*
Hardon, John A., S.J. *The Catholic Catechism*
_____. *Modern Catholic Dictionary*
_____. *The Question and Answer Catholic Catechism*
Hayes, Edward J., Hayes, Paul J. and Drummey, James J. *Catholicism and Life*
_____. *Catholicism and Reason*
_____. *Catholicism and Society*
John Paul II, Pope. *Evangelium Vitae* ("The Gospel of Life")
_____. *Reconciliatio et Paenitentia* ("Reconciliation and Penance")
_____. *Veritatis Splendor* ("The Splendor of Truth")
May, William E. *An Introduction to Moral Theology*
Vatican II. *Pastoral Constitution on the Church in the Modern World*
Wuerl, Donald, Lawler, Thomas and Lawler, Ronald. *The Catholic Catechism*
_____. *The Teaching of Christ*

Conditions Affecting Morality

Purpose: The purpose of this lesson is to show how certain factors can interfere with our knowledge and free will in committing an act and thereby diminish our guilt or eliminate it altogether.

Tips for Teachers: One way of starting this lesson is to ask what the conditions are for a mortal sin (e.g., grave matter, sufficient knowledge, and full consent of the will) and then to explain how certain factors or conditions can affect our knowledge and consent, thus lessening or even removing our guilt entirely. Take each of the seven conditions mentioned in the chapter and discuss them, using the charts where possible.

It will be important to describe the factors, and their subcategories, carefully so as not to give anyone an excuse for committing a sin. For example, in discussing ignorance, make sure to stress our obligation to dispel any ignorance, to take steps to enlighten ourselves as to whether a certain act is right or wrong. Note that it would be wrong *not* to seek further information if we knew that such information was available.

Concupiscence, which is our natural human inclination toward sin, is a most important factor in making moral decisions. It is a consequence of original sin (see section 1264 of the *Catechism of the Catholic Church* for some other consequences). Although Baptism takes away original sin, our human nature is weakened so that we have difficulty knowing right from wrong and also doing what we know to be right. Have the class read and discuss St. Paul's lament about this problem in Romans 7:15.

The teacher or facilitator can also talk about the passions or feelings that can incline us to do good or to commit evil. Sections 1762-1775 of the *Catechism* offer some good commentary on such passions as love, hatred, desire, fear, joy, sadness, and anger. Passions can also diminish our guilt, something that is recognized in our courts when they distinguish between first degree murder (one that is carefully premeditated) and second degree murder (one that results from a flareup of anger).

Habit is another area that needs to be carefully treated so that a person's inclination to commit a certain sin is not excused because his or her action is habitual. Masturbation is a classic example of a habitual action, and this section of the book offers a good opportunity for stating the Church's teaching and the reasons for that teaching. The Vatican's *Declaration on Certain Problems of Sexual Ethics* and Lawler, Boyle, and May's book *Catholic Sexual Ethics* will be helpful here.

Point out that habits, whether good ones or bad ones, are acquired by repetition and we can take steps to cultivate good habits and eliminate our bad ones. Ask for suggestions on how to do this.

Fear, violence, temperament, and nervous mental disorders also have a bearing on our moral choices. What this review of these conditions should tell us is not to judge the reason why people do certain things. We may say that a particular action — abortion, euthanasia, selling drugs — is wrong, but we cannot know the mental state or the moral awareness of the sinner, and therefore should leave the subjective guilt of that person to God, who knows their true state of mind.

Topics for Discussion:

1. Ignorance of the law is no excuse.
2. How can a Catholic overcome ignorance of how God wants us to live?
3. Which of the seven factors or conditions is the strongest influence on moral decision-making and why?
4. What remedies are there for overcoming concupiscence?
5. Which of the passions listed on pages 31-32 of the text would be the hardest to overcome?

Some Questions and Answers:

1. What are some of the consequences of original sin?
A. Although original sin is taken away by Baptism, certain lingering effects remain with us. For example, our minds are darkened so that we don't always see clearly what God

wants us to do, and our wills are weakened so that we often find it hard to do the right thing and easy to do the wrong thing. Here is what the *Catechism of the Catholic Church* says about this problem:

> Yet certain temporal consequences of sin remain in the baptized, such as suffering, illness, death, and such frailties inherent in life as weaknesses of character, and so on, as well as an inclination to sin that Tradition calls *concupiscence*, or metaphorically, "the tinder for sin" (*fomes peccati*); since concupiscence "is left for us to wrestle with, it cannot harm those who do not consent but manfully resist it by the grace of Jesus Christ." Indeed, "an athlete is not crowned unless he competes according to the rules" (n. 1264).

2. Why doesn't the Church get with the times and stop calling masturbation a sin?

A. For the same reason that the Church doesn't change its teachings on abortion, contraception, euthanasia, and a host of other evils to conform with the thinking of the times. The Church was established by Christ to give us the truth about moral issues, and it would be unfaithful to Christ to water down or ignore the truth that certain actions are contrary to God's plan, regardless of whether or not our culture agrees with the Creator's plan. People fall into a variety of bad habits, including masturbation, but we do a disservice to them to condone those habits or to say that it's okay to continue in them. If we truly love our brothers and sisters, we will try to help them overcome their bad habits by encouraging them to seek God's grace through the Sacraments. Nothing is impossible with God's help.

3. If Jesus said that we shouldn't judge others, why does the Church say that certain actions are wrong?

A. Jesus was referring to judging a person's motives, not his actions. We can say that a certain action, such as abortion, is wrong, without speculating on why this particular person chose to have an abortion. If someone steals your car, are you going to refrain from reporting it to the police lest you be considered judgmental? Of course not. There is nothing wrong with calling evil by its right name, but we should leave up to God the judgment of those who commit evil since only He knows why people do the things they do.

Projects:

1. Do a report on one of the references listed below.
2. Make a poster of one of the charts in the chapter under discussion and give an oral presentation on it.
3. Think of a bad habit and make some suggestions on how a person could overcome it.
4. Choose a good habit and work to strengthen it.
5. Keep track for one week of the number of times you make judgmental statements about other people and resolve to stop doing it.

References:

Catechism of the Catholic Church
Catholic Almanac
Catholic Encyclopedia. Edited by Fr. Peter M.J. Stravinskas
Drummey, James J. Catholic Replies
Encyclopedia of Catholic Doctrine. Edited by Russell Shaw
Flannery, Austin, O.P. Vatican Council II: The Conciliar
        and Post Conciliar Documents
Grisez, Germain. Christian Moral Principles
_____. Difficult Moral Questions
_____. Living a Christian Life
Hardon, John A., S.J. The Catholic Catechism
_____. Modern Catholic Dictionary
_____. The Question and Answer Catholic Catechism
Hayes, Edward J., Hayes, Paul J. and Drummey, James J.
        Catholicism and Life
_____. Catholicism and Reason
_____. Catholicism and Society
John Paul II, Pope. Evangelium Vitae ("The Gospel of Life")
_____. Reconciliatio et Paenitentia ("Reconciliation and
        Penance")
_____. Veritatis Splendor ("The Splendor of Truth")

May, William E. *An Introduction to Moral Theology*
Vatican II. Pastoral *Constitution on the Church in the
     Modern World*
Wuerl, Donald, Lawler, Thomas and Lawler, Ronald. *The
     Catholic Catechism*
_____. *The Teaching of Christ*

Natural Law and God's Law

Purpose: The purpose of this lesson is to show that our sources of moral guidance can be found in the natural law, the law of God as expressed in the Ten Commandments and the Sermon on the Mount, and in Church and civil law.

Tips for Teachers: Begin by asking the class to assume that they are the only survivors of a worldwide catastrophe and that they are faced with the task of rebuilding civilization. What laws would they make to insure that people could work together and get along while their new civilization is being constructed?

The specific laws that they come up with should stem from the natural law which God has built into human nature. It can be most simply stated as "Do good and avoid evil." Or as Jesus put it, "Treat others the way you would have them treat you" (Matthew 7:12).

Point out that natural law is really common sense, for how can a society survive unless persons respect the life, health, family, and property of others? Who would want to live in a society where murder, rape, theft, and violence were not punished? That is why people formed governments — to protect what the Declaration of Independence called our God-given rights to life, liberty, and the pursuit of happiness. Charles Rice's book *50 Questions on the Natural Law* is an excellent resource for this lesson.

Though men and women knew right from wrong before the Ten Commandments, God saw the need to make his plan for us more explicit and so he gave Moses the Decalogue. Have the students read this account in chapters 19-20 of the Book of Exodus, as well as the account of what Moses discovered had happened while he was receiving the two stone tablets from God on top of Mt. Sinai (chapter 32 of Exodus).

Have the students memorize the Ten Commandments. All Catholics should know this basic list of moral dos and don'ts.

If the teacher or facilitator has time, it would be profitable to discuss the many moral principles enunciated by Jesus in the Sermon on the Mount (chapters 5-7 of Matthew's Gospel). Jesus goes beyond the Ten Commandments in saying that it is not enough to say we have not murdered anyone or committed adultery; we must not even grow angry or look at someone lustfully. Jesus is not abolishing the old law, but rather showing us how it can be most completely fulfilled. Several lessons could be built around the Sermon on the Mount if time permits.

Another point is to show that our obedience to the natural law and to the Ten Commandments also extends to Church and civil law that is in accord with God's law. Remind the class of our duty to follow the Pope and the bishops in communion with him (Matthew 16:18). That is why the Popes so often issue important religious and moral documents, such as "The Splendor of Truth" and "The Gospel of Life," so that we will not lack clear moral guidance in confusing moral times.

Regarding laws passed by civil governments, we must obey them, too, provided that they conform to God's law. If they are contrary to divine law, e.g., the legalization of abortion, then we must "obey God rather than men!" (Acts 5:29). The Bishops of the United States, at their meeting in November 1998, reminded Catholic public officials of their responsibility regarding the protection of innocent human life:

> As is true of leaders in all walks of life, no political leader can evade accountability for his or her exercise of power (*Evangelium Vitae*, 73-74). Those who justify their inaction on the grounds that abortion is the law of the land need to recognize that there is a higher law, the law of God. No human law can validly contradict the commandment: "Thou shalt not kill."

Topics for Discussion:

1. If you could put one law into effect, what would it be?
2. How would you get people to obey your law?
3. Why did God give Moses the Ten Commandments?
4. Which of the Ten Commandments do you think is the most important and why?

5. How would you answer a Catholic who says, "I don't have to follow the laws of the Catholic Church"?

6. Give examples of treating others the way that we would want them to treat us.

7. Explain why it is better to obey God than men.

Some Questions and Answers:

1. What is the natural law?

A. The natural law, said St. Thomas Aquinas, "is nothing other than the light of understanding infused in us by God, whereby we understand what must be done and what must be avoided. God gave this light and this law to man at creation" (cf. *Veritatis Splendor*, n. 12). The natural law is written and engraved in our hearts and is a part of our nature. That is why even a young child who has done wrong feels uncomfortable, even if the child has never heard of the moral law. His reason indicates that some things are wrong, i.e., contrary to the natural law.

Natural law is also universal because, being based on human nature, it binds all of us. It is unchangeable because human nature is the same at all times and in all places. Therefore, all acts contrary to the natural law, such as murder, will always remain immoral. Human authorities can make murder legal, as in the case of abortion, but they can never make it moral.

The Ten Commandments are a summary of the principles of the natural law, but they do not contain all the details of the natural law. For example, "Honor your father and your mother" refers not just to our obligations to our parents, but also to all superiors and lawful authorities.

2. Why do Catholics number the Ten Commandments differently from other religions?

A. The enumeration of the Ten Commandments that appears in Exodus 20:1-17 and Deuteronomy 5:6-21 is longer and more detailed than the simple listing of the Decalogue that can be found in most religion books. This is particularly true with regard to what Catholics consider the first and second commandments. For instance, in the New American Bible (1970 edition), the first commandment says, "I, the Lord, am your God, *who brought you out of the land of Egypt, that place of slavery*. You shall not have other gods besides me" (Exodus 20:2-3). When stating the first commandment, we usually omit the italicized words.

You then have to go down to verse seven to get the second commandment: "You shall not take the name of the Lord, your God, in vain." In between verses three and seven is a command not to carve idols or to bow down before them or to worship them. Some religions have made these verses their second commandment, which makes our second commandment their third commandment, and so on. The total number of ten is maintained by combining into one commandment the prohibitions against coveting a neighbor's wife or goods (Exodus 20:17) that Catholics list as two separate commandments.

The most important thing to remember, however, is not the differences in the numbering system, but rather that Catholics, Protestants, and Jews agree on the entire moral blueprint handed down by God.

3. How do you answer someone who calls the Ten Commandments "Old Testament morality" that was replaced by Jesus' law of love in the New Testament?
A. You could quote Jesus' statement: "Do not think that I have come to abolish the law and the prophets. I have come not to abolish them, but to fulfill them" (Matthew 5:17). Or our Lord's statement when asked what a person must do to get to heaven: "Keep the commandments." When he was asked which commandments, Jesus replied: " 'You shall not kill'; 'You shall not commit adultery'; 'You shall not steal'; 'You shall not bear false witness'; 'Honor your father and your mother'; and 'Love your neighbor as yourself' " (Matthew 19:16-19).

For more insight into this, see sections 8-15 of "The Splendor of Truth," especially where Pope John Paul says:

> From the very lips of Jesus, the new Moses, man is once again given the commandments of the Decalogue. Jesus himself definitively confirms them and proposes them to us as the way and condition of salvation (n. 12).

See also sections 2052-2082 of the *Catechism of the Catholic Church* for more on the importance of the Decalogue.

Projects:

1. Do a report on one of the references listed below.
2. Read the Sermon on the Mount and list on a poster ten things that Jesus said to guide us.
3. Memorize the Ten Commandments.
4. Act out the dialogue between Jesus and the rich young man in Matthew 19:16-22.
5. Watch television for one week and list the violations of the Ten Commandments that are portrayed, often favorably.
6. Compose a Penance Service and encourage your class to go to the Sacrament of Penance.

References:

Catechism of the Catholic Church
Catholic Almanac
Catholic Encyclopedia. Edited by Fr. Peter M.J. Stravinskas
Drummey, James J. *Catholic Replies*
Encyclopedia of Catholic Doctrine. Edited by Russell Shaw
Flannery, Austin, O.P. *Vatican Council II: The Conciliar and Post Conciliar Documents*
Grisez, Germain. *Christian Moral Principles*
_____. *Difficult Moral Questions*
_____. *Living a Christian Life*
Hardon, John A., S.J. *The Catholic Catechism*
_____. *Modern Catholic Dictionary*
_____. *The Question and Answer Catholic Catechism*
Hayes, Edward J., Hayes, Paul J. and Drummey, James J. *Catholicism and Life*
_____. *Catholicism and Reason*
_____. *Catholicism and Society*
John Paul II, Pope. *Evangelium Vitae* ("The Gospel of Life")
_____. *Reconciliatio et Paenitentia* ("Reconciliation and Penance")
_____. *Veritatis Splendor* ("The Splendor of Truth")
May, William E. *An Introduction to Moral Theology*
Rice, Charles E. *50 Questions on the Natural Law*

Vatican II. Pastoral *Constitution on the Church in the Modern World*

Wuerl, Donald, Lawler, Thomas and Lawler, Ronald. *The Catholic Catechism*

_____. *The Teaching of Christ*

Forming a Right Conscience

Purpose: The purpose of this lesson is to explain what is meant by a right conscience and to stress our obligation to follow a conscience that has been correctly formed.

Tips for Teachers: Ask the class for ideas on what conscience means or for comments on the statement, "Let your conscience be your guide." The sections on conscience in "The Splendor of Truth" (nn. 32, 34, 54-64) and in the *Catechism of the Catholic Church* (nn. 1776-1802) will be helpful in preparing this lesson. Look for suggestions from the students on how to form a right conscience; the catechist cannot emphasize the words "right conscience" enough. Have them clip articles from newspapers and magazines, especially from so-called advice columns, to illustrate the kind of often-erroneous information that people rely on to make moral decisions.

Stress that conscience is like a computer ("garbage in, garbage out"), i.e., what goes into conscience determines what comes out, so accurate information is essential. Ask where accurate information can be found, and point to Scripture, Tradition, and the teaching office of the Church. Who did more teaching on a worldwide basis than Pope John Paul II? His constant message during more than 20 years of traveling to the far corners of the globe was a call to holiness. It was essentially the same message as that of Jesus: "Reform your lives and believe in the gospel!" (Mark 1:14-15).

After clearly defining conscience and showing how to form a correct conscience, the teacher or group leader can describe the different types of conscience, giving examples of each, and our obligations relative to conscience. We must follow a certain conscience, but not a doubtful one. Mention the importance of not kidding ourselves about which actions are good and which are bad.

It would be helpful to have the class go over and discuss both the Pope's statement on page 50 and the U.S. Bishops' statement on page 51.

Topics for Discussion:

1. Let your conscience be your guide.
2. How can we make sure that our conscience is correctly formed?
3. Explain the difference between a certain and a doubtful conscience.
4. What did Pope John Paul mean when he said (cf. page 50) that, for some people, conscience is just their "limited personal opinion"?

Some Questions and Answers:

1. How would you answer a person who says, "I don't have to listen to the Church in forming my conscience"?

A. Tell the person that since the Church speaks with the authority of Christ himself, and was called by St. Paul "the pillar and bulwark of truth" (1 Timothy 3:15), it only makes sense to follow what the Church says if one wants to stay close to God and get to heaven. Remember that Jesus told Peter, the first Pope, "Whatever you declare bound on earth shall be bound in heaven" (Matthew 16:19). And he told the disciples, "He who hears you, hears me. He who rejects you, rejects me. And he who rejects me, rejects him who sent me" (Luke 10:16). So we must follow the guidance of those to whom Jesus gave the authority to speak in his name since Jesus promised to ratify in heaven whatever laws they made on earth. Christ could have left us on our own to try to figure out the truth, but instead he gave us a sure and certain source of truth, the Catholic Church.

2. Who are some reliable sources of information when forming your conscience?

A. As we have mentioned above, the Church is a reliable source, and by the Church we mean the Pope and the bishops who are loyal to him, priests and deacons and nuns, religion teachers and group leaders, and family members and friends who are faithful Catholics. Unfortunately, there are some Catholics today who dissent from Church teaching and who present false or watered-down information about what the Bible and the Church have to say about religious and moral issues. When such a conflict arises, when what you are hearing from Father, or Sister, or Mr. or Mrs. Catechist doesn't sound right, then you must look to what the Holy Father says in his role as the Supreme Teacher in the Church. Follow his advice and not that of someone who says, in effect, "The Pope is a good man, but he's out of touch with the real world, so you don't really have to pay attention to him."

Projects:

1. Read sections 32, 34, and 54-64 of "The Splendor of Truth" and summarize the Pope's comments on conscience, picking out five important points he made.

2. Read sections 1776-1802 of the *Catechism of the Catholic Church* and choose five statements that deal with conscience.

3. Read the advice columns in the daily newspaper for a week and choose examples of both good and bad advice. By bad advice we mean recommendations of conduct that is contrary to what God and the Church teach.

4. Choose an issue and have different members of the class or group act out the various kinds of conscience (certain, doubtful, lax, scrupulous, tender).

References:

Catechism of the Catholic Church
Catholic Encyclopedia. Edited by Fr. Peter M.J. Stravinskas
Drummey, James J. *Catholic Replies*
Flannery, Austin, O.P. *Vatican Council II: The Conciliar
      and Post Conciliar Documents*
Grisez, Germain. *Christian Moral Principles*
_____. *Difficult Moral Questions*
_____. *Living a Christian Life*
Hardon, John A., S.J. *The Catholic Catechism*
_____. *Modern Catholic Dictionary*
_____. *The Question and Answer Catholic Catechism*
Hayes, Edward J., Hayes, Paul J. and Drummey, James J.
      Catholicism and Life
_____. *Catholicism and Reason*
_____. *Catholicism and Society*

John Paul II, Pope. *Evangelium Vitae* ("The Gospel of Life")
_____. *Reconciliatio et Paenitentia* ("Reconciliation and Penance")
_____. *Veritatis Splendor* ("The Splendor of Truth")
May, William E. *An Introduction to Moral Theology*
Vatican II. Pastoral *Constitution on the Church in the Modern World*
Wuerl, Donald, Lawler, Thomas and Lawler, Ronald. *The Catholic Catechism*
_____. *The Teaching of Christ*

Twofold or Double Effect

Purpose: The purpose of this lesson is to demonstrate the reasoning process involved in deciding whether to perform an act that has both good and bad effects.

Tips for Teachers: Begin by asking if the class can think of a situation when it would be all right to employ evil means to achieve a good end (there are no such situations, of course). Then ask for examples of actions that have both good and bad effects and for suggestions on how to decide whether it is morally right to perform the actions or not. Make sure to distinguish between performing a good act that has both good and bad effects, and an evil act that may have good results. Also, distinguish between what is willed or wanted by the person performing the act and what is only permitted or tolerated.

Having gone through these preliminary steps, the catechist can next spell out the four conditions that are necessary if the principle of the twofold or double effect is to be properly invoked. Write the conditions on the board or have one or more students make a poster listing the conditions.

After the conditions have been explained and discussed, start with an easy illustration of the principle, such as the example of the boy with the cut hand on page 55, and then move on to more complicated situations, such as the pregnant woman with the cancerous uterus.

Ask each student to come up with a case, either one that fits the four conditions or one that fails to do so. Go over each case carefully to show how the principle applies or does not apply.

Some other situations that the teacher or group leader could propose to the class include the following:

(1) A terminally ill patient is suffering from intense pain. The doctor proposes increasing the dose of narcotics to alleviate the pain, knowing that the pain-relief medicine could hasten the patient's death. Is it morally permissible to increase the

dosage? The answer is yes, since the act of giving medication is good, the good effect (pain relief) comes directly from the action and not from the evil effect (shortening the patient's life), the good effect is willed and the evil effect only tolerated, and there is a sufficient reason for permitting the evil effect to occur. The same would not be true, for example, if a doctor gave a life-shortening dose of narcotics to a person suffering from an ordinary headache.

(2) When American military forces were ordered onto the beaches of Normandy near the end of World War II, their leaders knew that many Americans would die in the D-Day landing, despite efforts to limit casualties. Was this military operation morally allowable under the principle of the twofold effect? Yes, because the act of liberating France from the Nazis was a good one, the good effect was not caused by the evil effect, the casualties were not willed but only tolerated, and the good effect far outweighed the evil effect.

(3) In chapter 11 of the Bible's 2nd Book of Samuel, King David wanted to get rid of Uriah the Hittite so that he could have his wife Bathsheba. To accomplish this, David ordered his military commander to put Uriah on the front lines of the battle so that he would certainly be killed. Was David's action morally permissible? No, because the act of putting Uriah in harm's way was evil, the "good" effect of getting Bathsheba was caused by the evil effect of having Uriah killed, the death of Uriah was definitely willed, and the evil effect was nowhere near equivalent to the "good" effect.

Topics for Discussion:

1. Is there ever a situation where it would be okay to use an evil means to achieve a good end?
2. Which of the four conditions of the double effect is the most important and why?
3. Discuss an action that you have performed, seen, or read about that had both a good effect and an evil effect.
4. Why are people today so willing to approve evil means to bring about a purported good?

Some Questions and Answers:

1. Where did the principle of the twofold or double effect originate?
A. The principle has been used in Catholic moral theology at least since the 17th century. You can find more information about the double effect in Germain Grisez's book *Christian Moral Principles* (cf. pp. 239-241, 298-300).

Projects:

1. Make a chart or poster showing the four conditions of the principle of the twofold effect.
2. Make a chart of a case where the principle can be validly applied (see pp. 57, 59 of the text for examples)
3. Make a chart of a situation where the principle cannot be validly applied (see pp. 57, 59 of the text for examples).
4. Look up sections 1753, 1756, 1759, and 1789 in the *Catechism of the Catholic Church* and put together an oral presentation explaining or defending one of those sections.

References:

Catechism of the Catholic Church
Catholic Almanac
Catholic Encyclopedia. Edited by Fr. Peter M.J. Stravinskas
Drummey, James J. Catholic Replies
Encyclopedia of Catholic Doctrine. Edited by Russell Shaw
Flannery, Austin, O.P. Vatican Council II: The Conciliar
       and Post Conciliar Documents
Grisez, Germain. Christian Moral Principles
_____. Difficult Moral Questions
_____. Living a Christian Life
Hardon, John A., S.J. The Catholic Catechism
_____. Modern Catholic Dictionary
_____. The Question and Answer Catholic Catechism
Hayes, Edward J., Hayes, Paul J. and Drummey, James J.
       Catholicism and Life
_____. Catholicism and Reason
_____. Catholicism and Society

John Paul II, Pope. *Evangelium Vitae* ("The Gospel of Life")
_____. *Reconciliatio et Paenitentia* ("Reconciliation and
        Penance")
_____. *Veritatis Splendor* ("The Splendor of Truth")
May, William E. *An Introduction to Moral Theology*
Vatican II. Pastoral *Constitution on the Church in the
        Modern World*
Wuerl, Donald, Lawler, Thomas and Lawler, Ronald. *The
        Catholic Catechism*
_____. *The Teaching of Christ*

Ordinary vs. Extraordinary Means

Purpose: The purpose of this lesson is to make clear the important distinction between using ordinary means and extraordinary means to preserve one's life and health.

Tips for Teachers: First, make clear the principle that all of us have the right to all the necessary means to preserve our life and health, and then ask the class what some necessary means might be. Establish a definition of ordinary means (cf. page 63 of the text) and note that, depending on the person, place, time, and culture, one is usually bound to use such ordinary means as food, water, medicine, painkillers, routine surgery, etc. Point out, however, that not even these are required if they are clearly useless (in an imminently dying patient) or if they would constitute an unreasonable burden to the patient.

Explain the distinction between ordinary and extraordinary means and ask for examples of the latter. Emphasize that there is no obligation to use extraordinary means, either on the part of a conscious patient or those who are authorized to speak for him should he be unconscious or incompetent, unless the patient is indispensable to his family and their well-being or is not spiritually prepared for death.

For a clarification of what constitutes extraordinary means, see the information under "Some Questions and Answers."

Stress that the doctor's rights and duties are correlative with those of the patient and that the physician is not authorized to act on his own. He must follow the explicit wishes of his patient as expressed either directly to the doctor or indirectly through a health care agent.

Talk about "do not resuscitate" orders (DNR) and make clear that discontinuing resuscitation efforts is permissible if that is the wish of the patient since this kind of care is extraordinary means. This is not euthanasia, but rather accepting the human condition in the face of death, as Pope John Paul said.

Students ought to be assigned readings in "The Gospel of

Life," the Vatican's *Declaration on Euthanasia*, the documents from the Pontifical Council for Pastoral Assistance and the U.S. Catholic Bishops, and the pertinent sections of the *Catechism of the Catholic Church*. Oral reports or even debates on these matters would be useful in clarifying them for the class, as well as making the students articulate in defending the Church's position.

Another distinction that must be made is between what the medical profession considers ordinary means and what moral theologians think. What is medically ordinary might be ethically extraordinary, as Fr. Russell Smith points out (cf. page 63 of the text). Go over carefully Fr. Smith's explanation of what constitutes ordinary means (cf. page 64), and have the students memorize paragraph 2278 from the *Catechism* because it states the Church's teaching so clearly.

Finally, go over the seven norms that are listed on pages 64-65, asking which one is the most important, since they offer a good summary of the entire lesson.

Topics for Discussion:

1. Doctors should have the final say on whether a patient lives or dies.

2. If a person is a burden to his or her family, or is using valuable resources in a hospital or nursing home, then his or her medical care should be terminated.

3. What are some ordinary means of health care?

4. What are some extraordinary means of health care?

5. Should hospitals and nursing homes have to follow a patient's "do not resuscitate" order?

6. What kind of care would you like if you were suffering from a terminal illness?

7. What is wrong with "overzealous" treatment?

Some Questions and Answers:

1. **What are some extraordinary means that are acceptable to prolong life?**

A. It is difficult to enumerate extraordinary means of prolonging life because advances in medicine keep changing the definition of what is ordinary and what is extraordinary.

Surgical procedures once considered extraordinary are now fairly routine. In its 1980 *Declaration on Euthanasia*, the Sacred Congregation for the Doctrine of the Faith said that the best way to make a correct judgment in these matters is "by studying the type of treatment to be used, its degree of complexity or risk, its cost and the possibilities of using it, and comparing these with the result that can be expected, taking into account the state of the sick person and his or her physical and moral resources."

The Congregation went on to offer several clarifications of the general principles:

— A patient may choose the latest medical techniques, even if they are risky and still in the experimental stage.

— The patient may halt the use of these advanced techniques if they are not achieving the desired results or if they are imposing on the patient "strain or suffering out of proportion with the benefits which he or she may gain from such techniques."

— One can refuse advanced medical treatment and make do with normal means as an "acceptance of the human condition," to avoid medical procedures disproportionate to the results that can be expected, or to spare the family or the community excessive expenses.

— When death is imminent, the patient can refuse forms of treatment "that would only secure a precarious and burdensome prolongation of life, so long as the normal care due to the sick person in similar cases is not interrupted."

2. Are life-support measures mandatory or optional in near-death medical emergencies?

A. On April 2, 1992, the U.S. Bishops' Committee on Pro-Life Activities issued a statement on artificial nutrition and hydration that included the following guidelines:

> Everyone has the duty to care for his or her own life and health and to seek necessary medical care from others, but this does not mean that all possible remedies must be used in all circumstances. One is not obliged to use either 'extraordinary' means or 'disproportionate' means

of preserving life — that is, means which are understood as offering no reasonable hope of benefit or as involving excessive burdens. Decisions regarding such means are complex, and should ordinarily be made by the patient in consultation with his or her family, chaplain or pastor, and physician when that is possible. In the final stage of dying, one is not obliged to prolong the life of a patient by every possible means."

Projects:

1. Visit a chronic care hospital or nursing home.

2. Interview a nurse at one of these places and ask what they consider to be ordinary and extraordinary means.

3. Assign different students to read the documents mentioned earlier and in the references and give an oral report on some key sections or points.

4. Find out the Church's teaching on suffering (see chapter 10 of *Catholicism and Ethics*) and explain it to the class.

5. Make a chart showing Fr. Smith's list of the common elements used to determine what is ordinary means.

References:

Catechism of the Catholic Church
Catholic Almanac
Catholic Encyclopedia. Edited by Fr. Peter M.J. Stravinskas
Drummey, James J. *Catholic Replies*
Flannery, Austin, O.P. *Vatican Council II: The Conciliar
        and Post Conciliar Documents*
Grisez, Germain. *Christian Moral Principles*
_____. *Difficult Moral Questions*
_____. *Living a Christian Life*
Hardon, John A., S.J. *The Catholic Catechism*
_____. *Modern Catholic Dictionary*
_____. *The Question and Answer Catholic Catechism*
Hayes, Edward J., Hayes, Paul J. and Drummey, James J.
        Catholicism and Life
_____. *Catholicism and Reason*
_____. *Catholicism and Society*

John Paul II, Pope. *Evangelium Vitae* ("The Gospel of Life")
_____. *Reconciliatio et Paenitentia* ("Reconciliation and Penance")
_____. *Salvifici Doloris* ("On the Christian Meaning of Suffering")
_____. *Veritatis Splendor* ("The Splendor of Truth")
Kreeft, Peter. *Making Sense Out of Suffering*
May, William E. *An Introduction to Moral Theology*
Rice, Charles E. *50 Questions on Abortion, Euthanasia and Related Issues*
Smith, Wesley J. *Forced Exit*
Vatican II. Pastoral *Constitution on the Church in the Modern World*
Wuerl, Donald, Lawler, Thomas and Lawler, Ronald. *The Catholic Catechism*
_____. *The Teaching of Christ*

Moral Guides and Maxims

Purpose: The purpose of this lesson is to show that there are many words of wisdom from natural law, Scripture, and common sense that can help us make good moral and ethical decisions.

Tips for Teachers: The best thing to do with this lesson is simply to go through the 15 moral guides and maxims, using the examples in the chapter but also looking for other examples, as well as other maxims, from the students. You could also assign the students to read different sections of the Book of Proverbs in the Bible. There are hundreds of wise sayings in that book.

If you want to have some fun with the class, you could give each student one half of a proverb and ask him or her to come up with the rest of the saying. Here are some examples of well-known proverbs that were given new and often humorous endings by students:

Better to be safe than .... punch a senior.
Strike while the .... bug is close.
It's always darkest before .... daylight savings time.
Never underestimate the power of .... termites.
You can lead a horse to water but .... how?
Don't bite the hand that .... looks dirty.
No news is .... impossible.
A miss is as good as a .... Mr.
You can't teach an old dog new .... math.
The pen is mightier than the .... pigs.
An idle mind is .... the best way to relax.
Where there's smoke, there's .... pollution.
A penny saved is .... not much.
Two's company, three's .... the Musketeers.
Don't put off till tomorrow what .... you wore to bed.
Children should be seen and not .... spanked.
If at first you don't succeed .... get new batteries.
When the blind leads the blind .... get out of the way.

You get out of something .... what you see on the box.
Laugh and the world laughs with you, cry and .... you
have to blow your nose.

Topics for Discussion:

1. Does the end ever justify the means?
2. No one should act as a judge in his own case.
3. No one is held to the impossible.
4. The salvation of souls is the highest law.

Some Questions and Answers:

1. What do you mean by the "spirit of Vatican II" contradicting the letter of the Council?

A. In the years following the Second Vatican Council, there was considerable confusion among Catholics about changes in the Church. The confusion was partly due to individuals making statements and inaugurating changes on the grounds that they were sanctioned by the "spirit of Vatican II." In point of fact, however, there was nothing in the official record of the Council, as expressed in its 16 documents, to justify some of the statements made or some of the changes introduced. As the late Bishop George Ahr of Trenton often said: "The spirit of Vatican II is what the words of Vatican II say."

The confusion was particularly prevalent in the field of religious education, and catechists involved in teaching the Faith in those days can surely recall hearing some rather bizarre pronouncements from persons who were presumed to be speaking accurately about what the Council had said. One of the authors of this book, for example, remembers being told at a training session for catechists that there was no reason to require children to memorize the Our Father since that prayer really wasn't all that important. This about the only prayer that Jesus taught us!

One of the reasons for the publication of the *Catechism of the Catholic Church* in 1992 was to help end nearly three decades of confusion. Pope John Paul said that the *Catechism* was given to the Church to be "a sure and authentic reference text for teaching Catholic doctrine," to help the faithful "who wish to deepen their knowledge of the unfathomable riches of salvation," and to inform every individual "who asks us to give an account of the hope that is in us (cf. 1 Peter 3:15) and who wants to know what the Catholic Church believes." By the way, the *Catechism* devoted 107 paragraphs to a discussion of the Our Father, which it called "the most perfect of prayers."

Projects:

1. Have each student come up with his or her own maxim.
2. Assign the students different sections of the Book of Proverbs and have them give an oral report to the class on several proverbs that they found to be pertinent to life today.

References:

Catechism of the Catholic Church
Catholic Almanac
Catholic Encyclopedia. Edited by Fr. Peter M.J. Stravinskas
Drummey, James J. *Catholic Replies*
Encyclopedia of Catholic Doctrine. Edited by Russell Shaw
Flannery, Austin, O.P. *Vatican Council II: The Conciliar and Post Conciliar Documents*
Grisez, Germain. *Christian Moral Principles*
_____. *Difficult Moral Questions*
_____. *Living a Christian Life*
Hardon, John A., S.J. *The Catholic Catechism*
_____. *Modern Catholic Dictionary*
_____. *The Question and Answer Catholic Catechism*
John Paul II, Pope. *Evangelium Vitae* ("The Gospel of Life")
_____. *Veritatis Splendor* ("The Splendor of Truth")
May, William E. *An Introduction to Moral Theology*
Wuerl, Donald, Lawler, Thomas and Lawler, Ronald. *The Catholic Catechism*
_____. *The Teaching of Christ*

Cooperation in Evil

Purpose: The purpose of this lesson is to show the principles that we must follow to avoid cooperating in the evil actions of others.

Tips for Teachers: Using the quotation from the *Catechism of the Catholic Church* at the head of the chapter as a starting point, ask for examples of leading people into sin. Review the sin of scandal by referring to pages 94-95 of *Catholicism and Life*, a companion volume in this series. Note that scandal is a sin against the Fifth Commandment, which not only forbids killing the body of another person but also killing the life of God in that person's soul by leading him or her to commit a mortal sin.

Additional helpful references include sections 2284-2287 of the *Catechism* and Jesus' warning against scandal in Matthew 18:5-7 and Luke 17:1-2. Have the students read and discuss these references.

Next, ask for examples of cooperation in evil and explain the distinction between formal cooperation, where we actually share in the evil intention of the principal agent, and material cooperation, where our act is not wrong in itself, but it could be used by the principal agent to help him commit the evil act.

Ask the class for examples of both kinds of cooperation (see the examples below), stress that formal cooperation is never allowed, and show that material cooperation may be allowed if there is a sufficient and proportionate reason. The chart on page 74 of the text can be used to illustrate the difference.

The nine ways of cooperating in sin should stimulate an interesting discussion. Ask which is the most important or serious and why, and elicit examples of each of the nine ways from the students. A couple of students could be assigned to come up with two examples of each way.

The writings of Germain Grisez, a moral theologian who is loyal to the magisterium of the Catholic Church, would be helpful with this lesson, especially appendix 2 of his book *Difficult Moral Questions*, pages 871-897, which is entitled "Formal and material cooperation in others' wrongdoing."

Topics for Discussion:

1. A classmate who is failing algebra wants you to help him get a copy of the final exam so that he can pass the course and graduate. He wants you to engage the teacher in conversation while he downloads the exam from the teacher's computer. Are you allowed to cooperate in this way?

2. There was a movie on television about experimentation on homeless persons kidnapped off the streets in order to bring about a cure for those paralyzed by spinal injuries. The doctor in charge, who is the father of a paralyzed child and is very close to a medical breakthrough, tries to convince a researcher to take part in the program. He says that no one will miss any of the homeless subjects and that sacrificing a few of them will mean thousands of paralyzed people will be able to walk again. Can the researcher cooperate in this type of a program?

3. A person who works in a video store sometimes has to rent out videos from the x-rated section in a back room. He does not like doing this, but he needs the money and isn't sure he could easily get another job. May he continue to work in that store?

4. A pro-life pharmacist is asked to fill prescriptions for birth control pills and devices that he knows can cause pregnant women to have an early abortion. Is he allowed to fill those prescriptions?

Some Questions and Answers:

1. Is it wrong to hold shares in a company which makes and sells contraceptives and abortion-producing drugs or to invest in government bonds when the U.S. Government spends large sums of money funding abortion agencies?

A. Obviously one cannot cooperate formally in evil, i.e., to will or share in the evil intention by, say, giving money directly to Planned Parenthood, the nation's largest baby-killing conglomerate, or buying or continuing to hold a large number of shares in a company that is actively supporting immoral activities.

But there is also material cooperation, in which a person does not will or intend the evil but knows that some of his funds could be used for evil activities. The morality of this cooperation depends on how close one is to the immoral action (proximate or remote) and whether there is a proportionate reason for the cooperation. The more necessary one's material cooperation is to the act, the graver must be the reason to justify it morally.

Since large corporations and the government can still accomplish their immoral activities without the assistance of an individual's money, then his cooperation would be remote and only an ordinary or slight reason would be sufficient to justify holding shares in a company or buying government securities. But there is still the question of whether one should do this at all.

In his book *Difficult Moral Questions*, respected moral theologian Germain Grisez lists several conditions that must be met for acceptable material cooperation in purchasing or holding stocks or bonds. For example, he says that one must have a justified need for investing in some way and must have concluded, after a reasonable investigation, that this company's stocks or the government's securities are the best way of meeting that need or that investing in another adequate alternative would raise similar problems.

Second, one should steer clear of investments that are heavily tainted with immoral activities, such as a company that is well known for its production of abortion-producing drugs or devices, or the Federal Government, which contributes millions of dollars to anti-life agencies like Planned Parenthood or to the shipment of contraceptives and abortifacients to Third World nations.

Third, one must resist the temptation to take into account the profitability of certain investments if that profitability depends on something immoral.

In light of these conditions, a Catholic who wants to avoid any cooperation in morally tainted activities should refrain from buying shares in certain companies and from investing in government bonds. That is the only sure way to guarantee that one's money is not being used, even in a small way, to promote immoral actions.

Projects:

1. Make a poster of the chart on page 74 of the text.
2. Make a poster illustrating another example of formal and material cooperation.
3. Make a poster of the nine ways of cooperating in sin and elicit from the class examples of each way.
4. Choose one of the 200 *Difficult Moral Questions* in Germain Grisez's book and summarize the problem and present his solution.

References:

Catechism of the Catholic Church
Catholic Almanac
Catholic Encyclopedia. Edited by Fr. Peter M.J. Stravinskas
Drummey, James J. *Catholic Replies*
Encyclopedia of Catholic Doctrine. Edited by Russell Shaw
Flannery, Austin, O.P. *Vatican Council II: The Conciliar
        and Post Conciliar Documents*
Grisez, Germain. *Christian Moral Principles*
_____. *Difficult Moral Questions*
_____. *Living a Christian Life*
Hardon, John A., S.J. *The Catholic Catechism*
_____. *Modern Catholic Dictionary*
_____. *The Question and Answer Catholic Catechism*
Hayes, Edward J., Hayes, Paul J. and Drummey, James J.
        Catholicism and Life
_____. *Catholicism and Reason*
_____. *Catholicism and Society*
John Paul II, Pope. *Evangelium Vitae* ("The Gospel of Life")
_____. *Veritatis Splendor* ("The Splendor of Truth")
May, William E. *An Introduction to Moral Theology*
Wuerl, Donald, Lawler, Thomas and Lawler, Ronald. *The
        Catholic Catechism*
_____. *The Teaching of Christ*

Opposition to Contraception

Purpose: The purpose of this lesson is to show the unbroken tradition of Christian opposition to artificial means of contraception until 1930 and the continuing Catholic opposition since then.

Tips for Teachers: There are few teachings of the Catholic Church that are more misunderstood or opposed than its prohibition of artificial methods of contraception. The Church's Magisterium or teaching office has never backed away from this teaching on the origins of human life, but the teaching has often been ignored, undermined, or rejected by Catholics in positions to influence others about this issue.

So it is important for the catechist or group leader to show the historical background of the ban on artificial contraception, as well as the sound moral and practical reasons for it. In addition to Church documents themselves, also valuable are the writings of Janet Smith, John Kippley, and Brian Clowes that are mentioned in the text and in the references at the end of this lesson.

There are no guarantees that students will be persuaded by the information in this and subsequent lessons, especially since they hear so many false and distorted views from those in the media and those who dissent from the Church's teaching. But at least in this and subsequent classes you will have the opportunity to give them a coherent presentation of God's plan for bringing new life into the world.

Don't cut any corners or leave out any information. Give them all the necessary background and facts and let the Holy Spirit inspire them to understand and accept this teaching.

Begin the class by noting the unanimous opposition of Christian churches to contraception until the Lambeth Conference in England in 1930. Show how the Lambeth break with tradition quickly spread to the United States, how even a secular newspaper like the *Washington Post* recognized the significance of the Lambeth decision, and then trace what has happened since then, culminating in the Supreme Court's *Roe v. Wade* decision in 1973 that legalized abortion for any reason whatsoever for all nine months of pregnancy.

Review the seven guidelines on page 81 of the text before tracing the unbroken Catholic moral tradition against artificial methods of contraception. Ask which guideline is the most important and why.

Beginning with the Genesis account of Onan's sin, follow the ban on contraceptive actions through the Apostles (the *Didache*), St. Augustine, St. Thomas Aquinas, and up through 20th century Popes, starting with Pius XI, who responded immediately to the Lambeth decision with his encyclical on Christian marriage (*Casti Connubii*). If you have time, get a copy of that encyclical and go over the key parts with the class.

Point out, too, that many Protestant theologians, including Martin Luther and John Calvin, were foes of contraception (cf. Charles Provan's book *The Bible and Birth Control*).

The opposition of the Catholic Church was continued by Popes Pius XII and John XXIII, as well as the Second Vatican Council. Have the class take a close look at sections 47-52 of Vatican II's "Pastoral Constitution on the Church in the Modern World" (*Gaudium et Spes*), which came out in 1965, so that they will know that the Council not only did not move away from this important teaching, but solidly reaffirmed it.

Anyone paying attention to this constant reiteration and reaffirmation of the Church's teaching could not logically have expected that the Church would all of a sudden jettison its centuries-old ban on contraception. Nevertheless, many Catholics were falsely led to believe that the teaching would change, and so instead of rallying behind Pope Paul VI when he restated it in 1968, some Catholics attacked the Holy Father as being hopelessly out of touch with the modern world. We will see in the next lesson who was really out of touch.

Topics for Discussion:

1. Opposition to artificial birth control has always been strictly a Catholic position.

2. Since God is the sole Author of life, we cannot do whatever we want regarding the origins of human life.

3. What has happened since 1931 to prove that the editorial in the *Washington Post* was right?

4. If you could promote on national television one of the guidelines on page 81, which one would you choose?

5. Why did Pope Pius XI call contraception a "foul stain" on the married state?

Some Questions and Answers:

1. A priest says that we must always follow our conscience and, if our conscience tells us that artificial birth control is all right, then we are free to practice it. Is this true?

A. No, it is not true, and here are the reasons why. First, every conjugal act must be open to the transmission of life. This teaching has been constantly set forth by the Magisterium of the Church and will never change because it is rooted in the nature of man and woman. Second, while the sinfulness of those who practice birth control may be diminished if they are ignorant of or misled about the Church's teaching, or if the full consent of the will is not given, contraception itself is always objectively evil. It is up to the priest in Confession to determine whether the state of mind of the penitent has lessened the sinfulness of the action.

Third, the concept of conscience must be correctly understood. Conscience may be defined as a practical judgment as to whether an action is right or wrong. The key factor, however, is the way in which we arrive at this practical judgment. Do we consider the opinion of friends? Do we consult the advice columns in the newspaper? Do we try to determine what the Church teaches? Do we give equal weight to all of these sources?

The Catholic response to these questions is that our conscience must be formed according to the law of God, as authentically interpreted by the Catholic Church. We are always expected to follow our conscience, but it must be a right conscience, an informed conscience, a conscience that is in tune with the authoritative teaching of the Church, as expressed by the Holy Father. So if one's conscience is contrary to the teaching of the Pope, then one had better reconsider the steps that were taken, and the sources that were consulted, in arriving at an erroneous practical judgment.

2. How do you anwer someone who says that Vatican II opened the door to approval of contraception?

A. Tell this person to read the words of Vatican II on contraception! For example, *Gaudium et Spes* said that faithful members of the Church "may not undertake methods of regulating procreation which are found blameworthy by the teaching authority of the Church in its unfolding of the divine law" (n. 51). A footnote to that paragraph cited Pius XI's encyclical *Casti Connubii*, in which the Holy Father said that those who practice contraception "sin against nature and commit a deed which is shameful and intrinsically vicious" (n. 54), and Pius XII's speech to Italian midwives on October 29, 1951, in which he declared that "any attempt on the part of married people to deprive this act of its inherent force and to impede the procreation of new life, either in the performance of the act itself or in the course of the development of its natural consequences, is immoral."

Pius XII also said that "this precept is as valid today as it was yesterday; and it will be the same tomorrow and always, because it does not imply a precept of the human law but is the expression of a law which is natural and divine."

3. But if my daughter is going to be sexually active, wouldn't it make sense to put her on the contraceptive Pill?

A. No, for several reasons. First, you would show no trust or confidence in your daughter if you say to her, in effect, "You are nothing more than an animal with no control over your actions. You are not capable of saying no to sex before marriage." Giving her a contraceptive is like telling her it's okay to drink and drive as long as she wears a seat belt. Yes, too many teenagers are having sex, but the majority of teenagers are not. We need to hammer home the point that purity is security and that one should save sex for marriage instead of falling for the lie of "safe sex."

Second, you would be encouraging her to put a powerful drug into her body, one that can have long-term and dangerous side effects on her life and health. Research studies show that the synthetic hormones in birth control pills can damage the DNA of the undeveloped breast cells in young girls, and that this can lead to breast cancer later in life.

Furthermore, says Dr. David Zava, a biochemist and breast cancer researcher for decades, "another problem with synthetic hormones is that they can create a state of anovulation — no ovulation. Suppressing ovulation deprives the body of the natural hormones produced by the ovary that are needed for proper growth and development."

He says that "when ovulation is suppressed for years by birth control pills, not only is the body deprived of its natural hormones, the ovary can forget how to ovulate. I have heard from many clinicians that their patients who took birth control pills for more than a few years are often infertile because they are no longer ovulating."

Finally, since the Pill sometimes functions as an abortifacient, you would really be giving your daughter permission to abort in the early stages of pregnancy any child that she might conceive.

Projects:

1. Bring into class three contraception-promoting articles or ads from current newspapers or magazines.

2. Show your pastor the information above and the chapter in the *Catholicism and Ethics* text and ask him to preach about the evils of contraception from the pulpit.

3. Prepare an article or an insert for your parish bulletin with quotations from Pius XI, Pius XII, and Vatican II.

References:

Catechism of the Catholic Church
Catholic Almanac
Catholic Encyclopedia. Edited by Fr. Peter M.J. Stravinskas
Clowes, Brian. *The Facts of Life*
Drummey, James J. *Catholic Replies*
Encyclopedia of Catholic Doctrine. Edited by Russell Shaw
Flannery, Austin, O.P. *Vatican Council II: The Conciliar and Post Conciliar Documents*

Grisez, Germain. *Christian Moral Principles*
_____. *Difficult Moral Questions*
_____. *Living a Christian Life*
Hardon, John A., S.J. *The Catholic Catechism*
_____. *Modern Catholic Dictionary*
_____. *The Question and Answer Catholic Catechism*
Hayes, Edward J., Hayes, Paul J. and Drummey, James J.
    Catholicism and Life
_____. *Catholicism and Reason*
_____. *Catholicism and Society*
John Paul II, Pope. *Evangelium Vitae* ("The Gospel of Life")
_____. *Veritatis Splendor* ("The Splendor of Truth")
Kippley, John. *Sex and the Marriage Covenant*
May, William E. *An Introduction to Moral Theology*
Pius XI, Pope. "On Christian Marriage" (*Casti Connubii*)
Smith, Janet E. *Humanae Vitae: A Generation Later*
Wuerl, Donald, Lawler, Thomas and Lawler, Ronald. *The Catholic Catechism*
    Catholic Catechism
_____. *The Teaching of Christ*

Paul VI and Humanae Vitae

Purpose: The purpose of this lesson is to acquaint students with what Pope Paul VI actually said in his landmark encyclical on human life (*Humanae Vitae*).

Tips for Teachers: Using either the excerpts in the chapter or a complete copy of *Humanae Vitae*, spend this lessson, and more if necessary, reading and discussing what Paul VI said in his controversial encyclical. Some of the points that ought to be emphasized include:

1. The true meaning of responsible parenthood.
2. That "each and every marriage act must remain open to the transmission of life."
3. The two meanings or purposes of marriage.
4. The importance of following God's plan for married love.
5. The illicit ways of regulating birth.
6. The licitness of Natural Family Planning.
7. The grave consequences that will follow widespread practice of contraception.
8. This is not only Church law, but divine and natural law.
9. The message to those in the field of science.
10. The message to Christian husbands and wives.
11. The message to doctors and medical personnel.
12. The message to priests.

Note especially that the Holy Father's predictions about grave consequences (n. 17) have certainly come true, and note, too, the serious obligation of priests "to expound this teaching without ambiguity" (nn. 28-29).

Topics for Discussion:

1. What are some factors husbands and wives should take into account when deciding how many children to have?
2. Which of the purposes of marriage is more important?

3. How can priests spread the teaching of *Humanae Vitae* more effectively?

4. How was Pope Paul able to predict so accurately the grave consequences of widespread contraception?

Some Questions and Answers:

1. How do we answer those who say that contraception is necessary to curb a "population explosion" that will use up the world's resources and cause overcrowding and mass starvation?

A. As Jacqueline Kasun has pointed out in her carefully documented book, *The War on Population*, these claims are without foundation. The world has abundant resources and there is no population explosion. In fact, says Dr. Stephen Mosher of the Population Research Institute, "There are now 79 countries — representing fully 40 percent of the world's population — with fertility rates below the 2.2 needed to sustain their present numbers" (*Catholic World Report*, January 1999, p. 36).

Those countries that are usually cited as critical areas do not have a problem of numbers, but a problem of failing to develop their resources properly, using modern technology and agricultural methods, because their governments are more interested in accumulating power and wealth than in improving the welfare of their citizens.

Humanity's long-term problem, says Mosher, "is not going to be too many children, but too few — too few children to fill the schools and universities, too few young people entering the work force, too few couples buying homes and second cars; in short, too few consumers and producers to drive the economy forward" (*Ibid.*, p. 37).

2. But Pope Paul never actually said that practicing contraception was a sin.

A. Sure he did, in the section of the encyclical directed to Christian husbands and wives: "Let them implore divine assistance by persevering prayer; above all, let them draw from the source of grace and charity in the Eucharist. And if sin should still keep its hold over them, let them not be discouraged, but rather have recourse with humble perseverance to the mercy of God, which is poured forth in the sacrament of Penance" (n. 25).

3. If the Catholic Church is opposed to artificial contraception, doesn't that mean that it expects couples to have a child every year?
A. Of course not. The Church wants couples to practice responsible parenthood, which means, according to Vatican II, that couples "thoughtfully take into account both their own welfare and that of their children, those already born and those which may be foreseen. For this accounting they will reckon with both the material and the spiritual conditions of the times as well as of their state in life. Finally, they will consult the interests of the family group, of temporal society, and of the Church herself" (*Pastoral Constitution on the Church in the Modern World*, n. 50).

The Council went on to say, however, that in "harmonizing conjugal love with the responsible transmission of life . . . sons of the Church may not undertake methods of regulating procreation which are found blameworthy by the teaching authority of the Church in its unfolding of the divine law" (n. 51).

In other words, the practice of responsible parenthood cannot involve the use of artificial methods of birth control, or sterilization, or abortion to limit the size of a family. For those who have serious reasons to space out the births of their children, the only acceptable recourse is Natural Family Planning, which means abstaining from marital relations during those days when a woman is fertile and capable of conceiving a child.

Not only is NFP safer than chemical means and more effective than mechanical means; it requires the loving cooperation of husband and wife, unlike contraceptive methods that place the burden of responsibility on one partner, usually the wife.

Projects:

1. Bring in three articles from newspapers or magazines showing where the predictions of Pope Paul have come true.

2. Write a 300-word summary of what you consider the most important points in *Humanae Vitae*.

3. Plan a prayer vigil or Eucharistic adoration to cultivate respect for human life and for God's plan for married love.

4. Ask your pastor to preach on *Humanae Vitae*.

References:

Catechism of the Catholic Church
Catholic Almanac
Catholic Encyclopedia. Edited by Fr. Peter M.J. Stravinskas
Clowes, Brian. *The Facts of Life*
Drummey, James J. *Catholic Replies*
Encyclopedia of Catholic Doctrine. Edited by Russell Shaw
Flannery, Austin, O.P. *Vatican Council II: The Conciliar and Post Conciliar Documents*
Grisez, Germain. *Christian Moral Principles*
_____. *Difficult Moral Questions*
_____. *Living a Christian Life*
Hardon, John A., S.J. *The Catholic Catechism*
_____. *Modern Catholic Dictionary*
_____. *The Question and Answer Catholic Catechism*
Hayes, Edward J., Hayes, Paul J. and Drummey, James J. *Catholicism and Life*
_____. *Catholicism and Reason*
_____. *Catholicism and Society*
John Paul II, Pope. *Evangelium Vitae* ("The Gospel of Life")
_____. *Reflections on Humanae Vitae: Statements of the Holy Father*
_____. *Veritatis Splendor* ("The Splendor of Truth")
Kippley, John. *Sex and the Marriage Covenant*
May, William E. *An Introduction to Moral Theology*
Paul VI, Pope. *Humanae Vitae* ("On Human Life")
Pius XI, Pope. "On Christian Marriage" (*Casti Connubii*)
Smith, Janet E. *Humanae Vitae: A Generation Later*
Vatican II. *Gaudium et Spes* ("Pastoral Constitution on the Church in the Modern World")
Wuerl, Donald, Lawler, Thomas and Lawler, Ronald. *The Catholic Catechism*
_____. *The Teaching of Christ*

Lesson 13 (pp. 92-97)

John Paul II and the Catechism

Purpose: The purpose of this lesson is to discuss the reaffirmation of the Church's teaching on artificial birth prevention by Pope John Paul II and the *Catechism of the Catholic Church* and to show the connection between contraception and abortion.

Tips for Teachers: No Pope in modern times spoke more often, more forcefully, or more convincingly on married life than Pope John Paul II. His statement to a group of priests in 1983 (cf. page 93) is as strong a condemnation of contraception as you will find.

But the Holy Father's most comprehensive treatment of married life and love can be found in *Familiaris Consortio* ("The Role of the Christian Family in the Modern World"). The catechist or group leader should spend as much time as they can spare going through this document. Three areas to concentrate on are those where John Paul:

(1) Stresses the constancy of the Church's teaching throughout history on the transmission of human life (n. 29).

(2) Reiterates Paul VI's warning about government coercion in favor of contraception (n. 30).

(3) Emphasizes the necessity of holiness and sacrifice by husbands and wives in order to fulfill their lofty vocation (n. 34).

One of the most important contributions the Holy Father made to the debate was to establish the connection between contraception and abortion, which he did so well in *Evangelium Vitae*, his encyclical on "The Gospel of Life" (n. 13). Supporters of contraception vigorously deny such a connection, so it is important to know the arguments that the Pope used to prove his point. Contraception and abortion are indeed fruits of the same evil tree and stem from the same hostility to new life.

Finally, the teacher should refer to the reaffirmation of Catholic teaching on this matter in section 2370 of the *Catechism of the Catholic Church*. Make the observation that the constancy of this teaching, especially since 1930, leaves no doubt about where the Church stands and makes absurd any claims that some future pope or council might change this teaching. Ask the students to draw up a list, or make a poster, of all the magisterial statements since 1930 to show how consistent and firm has been the Church's opposition to artificial contraception.

Topics for Discussion:

1. Is there any reason to think that the Catholic Church will change its teaching on contraception in the future?

2. Why did Pope John Paul speak so often on this issue?

3. What did he mean when he said that those who engage in contraceptive behavior put themselves in a situation where they think "it is lawful not to recognize God as God"?

4. If you were a priest and a penitent asked you in Confession what he or she could do to stop practicing birth control, what advice would you give that person?

Some Questions and Answers:

1. How would you answer someone who says that there would be fewer abortions if the Catholic Church permitted contraception?

A. Even if this were true, which it isn't, it is wrong to allow one evil to prevent another evil. The two evils are not the same — abortion takes a life already in existence, while contraception prevents a life from coming into existence, but the fact of the matter is that more contraception leads to more abortion. The reason for this is that those who practice contraception have a mentality that is hostile to new babies and, when the contraceptive fails to prevent pregnancy, abortion becomes the backup method to get rid of those unwanted babies. In the words of Charles E. Rice, "permissive abortion is essential to a contraceptive society."

Another factor is that some so-called contraceptives, such as the Pill and the intrauterine device (IUD), act as abortifacients. That is, if they don't prevent new life from being conceived, then they cause early abortions by rendering the wall of the uterus hostile to the tiny developing human embryo.

"It may be that many people use contraception with a view to excluding the subsequent temptation of abortion," said Pope John Paul. "But the negative values inherent in the 'contraceptive mentality' — which is very different from responsible parenthood lived in respect for the full truth of the conjugal act — are such that they in fact strengthen this temptation when an unwanted life is conceived" (*Evangelium Vitae*, n. 13).

2. Why are governments and some wealthy individuals so intent on coercing people into practicing contraception, having abortions, or being sterilized?
A. Some may be sincere in thinking that they are helping to curb population growth, which as we have already seen is not a real problem (many European countries, in fact, are experiencing a serious population *decline*), but others simply want to eliminate certain classes of people. In Communist China, for example, boys are considered more valuable to society, so girl babies are killed either before or after they are born.

But why are billionaires like Ted Turner, Bill Gates, and Warren Buffet giving hundreds of millions of dollars for population control? Dr. Stephen Mosher, president of the Population Research Institute and an authority on China's coercive policies, offered this explanation in the March 24, 1999 *Washington Times*:

> You have healthy white men spending hundreds of millions of dollars to contraceptualize, sterilize, and abort poor brown, yellow, and black women in the developing worlds. That's a scary thought. There are hidden undertones of racism in much of the population control movement. After all, it began as hysterical reactions to the fact that the populations of Latin America, Africa, and Asia were growing much more rapidly than North America and Europe.

John Kippley of the Couple to Couple League added this thought in the May-June 1999 issue of his publication *CCL Family Foundations*:

The greatest nightmare of these anti-people people is that the Catholic Church might get its act together. Just imagine if two-thirds of Catholic parents were generous in having children, practiced only Natural Family Planning when they needed spacing, and voted pro-life. They would attract millions of evangelical Christians to a similar lifestyle, and the ecclesial and national downward debacle would be reversed.

To get an idea of where this contraceptive mentality originated, consider some statements that were made by Margaret Sanger (1879-1966), the founder of the Birth Control League and the Planned Parenthood Federation of America.

Among other things, Sanger urged curbing the fertility of the "benign imbeciles" who make up the working class and "who encourage the defective and diseased elements of humanity in their reckless and irresponsible swarming and spawning." She said that "the chief issue of birth control" was "more children from the fit, less from the unfit."

She called for the "elimination of human weeds" and sterilization of "inferior races" and, in her book *Women and the New Race*, Sanger declared that "the most merciful thing a large family can do to one of its infant members is to kill it."

For more information on the policies and programs of Planned Parenthood, see the books *Grand Illusions* by George Grant and *Blessed Are the Barren* by Robert Marshall and Charles Donovan.

Projects:

1. Read *Familiaris Consortio* and summarize the major points made by Pope John Paul.

2. List on a poster all the restatements of the Church's ban on artificial contraception since 1930.

3. Act out a person confessing to a priest the sin of contraception and have the priest give advice based on the *Vade Mecum* discussed on page 93 of the text.

4. Write to your United States Senator or Representative and ask them to sponsor legislation to halt the use of taxpayers' money by the U.S. Government to impose population control programs on poor people in other parts of the world.

References:

Catechism of the Catholic Church
Catholic Encyclopedia. Edited by Fr. Peter M.J. Stravinskas
Clowes, Brian. *The Facts of Life*
Drummey, James J. *Catholic Replies*
Encyclopedia of Catholic Doctrine. Edited by Russell Shaw
Flannery, Austin, O.P. *Vatican Council II: The Conciliar
    and Post Conciliar Documents*
Grant, George. *Grand Illusions: The Legacy of Planned
    Parenthood*
Grisez, Germain. *Christian Moral Principles*
_____. *Difficult Moral Questions*
_____. *Living a Christian Life*
Hardon, John A., S.J. *The Catholic Catechism*
_____. *Modern Catholic Dictionary*
_____. *The Question and Answer Catholic Catechism*
Hayes, Edward J., Hayes, Paul J. and Drummey, James J.
    Catholicism and Life
_____. *Catholicism and Reason*
_____. *Catholicism and Society*
John Paul II, Pope. *Evangelium Vitae* ("The Gospel of Life")
_____. *Familiaris Consortio* ("The Role of the Christian
    Family in the Modern World")
_____. *Veritatis Splendor* ("The Splendor of Truth")
Kasun, Jacqueline. *The War Against Population*
Kippley, John. *Sex and the Marriage Covenant*
Marshall, Robert, and Donovan, Charles. *Blessed Are the
    Barren: The Social Policy of Planned Parenthood*
Paul VI, Pope. *Humanae Vitae* ("On Human Life")
Pius XI, Pope. "On Christian Marriage" (*Casti Connubii*)
Smith, Janet E. *Humanae Vitae: A Generation Later*
Vatican II. *Gaudium et Spes* ("Pastoral Constitution on the
    Church in the Modern World")

Contraception vs. NFP

Purpose: The purpose of this lesson is to show precisely what contraception means, how it differs from Natural Family Planning, and why NFP is a morally permissible way of spacing out births.

Tips for Teachers: Start this class by breaking down the definition of contraception on page 97 regarding actions taken before, during, or after marital intercourse and then discussing the various artificial ways of preventing conception. This is not a sex education class, and catechists need to be prudent in covering these matters, especially with high school students, so as not to encourage experimentation with these drugs and devices or to create an occasion of sin.

A key point to make is that some so-called contraceptives are not true contraceptives at all, i.e., their function is not to prevent conception. Rather, they are in fact abortifacients since they cause an early abortion of the tiny human person. This is one of the effects of the Pill, Norplant, and Depo-Provera, and the sole effect of RU-486 and the IUD. The dangerous side effects of these drugs and devices should be made known to the class, including their link with breast cancer, in order to counter the propaganda that young people are constantly hearing from the anti-life side.

Catechists wanting to be thoroughly informed on these harmful effects can get reliable information from such pro-life groups as the Couple to Couple League, 4290 Delhi Pike, Cincinnati, OH 45238.

The next part of the lesson involves making the moral distinction between procedures aimed specifically at preventing conception and those which are aimed at correcting a problem with the procreative faculties. The latter situation is permissible, under the principle of the double effect, if the intention is to cure or alleviate a serious pathological condition. However, if the condition can be treated without contraceptives, then the twofold effect would not be applicable.

Immoral surgical means of preventing conception, such as vasectomy or tubal ligation, will be discussed in connection with sterilization when we get to chapter 9 in the text and lesson 19 in the manual.

The next segment deals with moral methods of spacing out births, either total abstinence or periodic abstinence, also known as Natural Family Planning. It is important to note that couples must have serious reasons to use NFP. By the way, this is not the same thing as the old calendar method of trying to determine when a woman was fertile, which was called rhythm and which often failed.

NFP is a very reliable method of spacing out births, and it is also safe, healthy, and inexpensive. Furthermore, it is wonderful for stable marriages since it requires mutual love, communication, and sacrifice by both spouses instead of placing all the burden on one spouse.

The Church's endorsement of this method is not new, but goes back to Pope Pius XI in 1930. It has since been given approval by Popes Pius XII and John Paul II, as well as by the Second Vatican Council and the *Catechism of the Catholic Church*. The Couple to Couple League is a very good source of information on NFP, particularly through its book *The Art of Natural Family Planning*, which was written by John and Sheila Kippley.

The other important component of this lesson is to demonstrate the difference between preventing conception by natural methods and by artificial methods. Some people claim that both approaches are morally the same. That this claim is false can be proven from the writings of Pope John Paul in *Familiaris Consortio* and John Kippley in *Sex and the Marriage Covenant*.

Topics for Discussion:

1. What are the three major categories of contraceptive methods?

2. Explain the difference between a contraceptive and an abortifacient.

3. Using the principle of the double effect, show under what conditions a person could use a contraceptive medication without incurring sin.

4. What is a major benefit of Natural Family Planning?

5. What do you think of this statement from the famous Hindu leader Mohandas Gandhi: "Contraceptives are an insult to womanhood. The difference between a prostitute and a woman using contraceptives is only that the former sells her body to several men, the latter sells it to one man"?

Some Questions and Answers:

1. Since the objective of both artificial contraception and Natural Family Planning is to avoid pregnancy, why does the Church support the natural form when it clearly has the same objective as the artificial means?

A. Both methods do indeed aim to avoid pregnancy, but morally they are not the same. Contraception involves taking direct and deliberate steps before, during, or after the marital act to prevent pregnancy. Natural Family Planning involves no marital act at all. In other words, contraception means doing something, while NFP means doing nothing.

There's a big difference, morally speaking, between acting against something and not acting at all. In the case of a terminal cancer patient, for example, it would be morally wrong to kill the patient with a drug injection, but it would not be wrong to forego an operation that at best might only keep the patient alive for a short time, that would be very costly, and that would cause the patient additional suffering.

A couple who for serious reasons seeks to practice responsible parenthood by spacing out the births of their children can abstain from marital relations without harboring a hostile and immoral attitude toward human life. They are not attacking life at its very beginning through chemical or mechanical means, but are rather allowing every marital act to remain open to the transmission of life.

Another significant difference between contraception and NFP is that the latter method requires the loving cooperation of both parties instead of placing the burden only on one partner. This mutual involvement of husband and wife, which will demand real communication between them, can enhance the respect, increase the affection, and deepen the love that they feel for each other.

2. What are some serious reasons that would justify using Natural Family Planning?

A. According to Vatican II's "Pastoral Constitution on the Church in the Modern World" (*Gaudium et Spes*), couples wishing to plan their family in a responsible (and moral) way may "thoughtfully take into account both their own welfare and that of their children, those already born and those which may be foreseen. For this accounting they will reckon with both the material and the spiritual conditions of the times, as well as of their state in life. Finally, they will consult the interests of the family group, of temporal society, and of the Church herself" (n. 50).

Consultation with a priest who is loyal to the magisterial teaching on human life would also guarantee that the married couple in question was being honest with themselves and with God and that their motives were truly serious enough to justify the use of NFP.

3. Can you give examples of dangerous side effects from using contraceptives?

A. In addition to the ones mentioned on pages 65-66 of this manual, the *John R. Lee, M.D. Medical Letter* for April 1999 reported a newly discovered danger for women who use Depo-Provera:

> Young women who use the injectable contraceptive Depo-Provera actually lose bone mass at a time in their lives when they should still be building it. The bone loss was especially steep (around 10 percent) in younger women age 18-21.

It is Dr. Lee's opinion that "the synthetic progestin used in the injections is most likely blocking the bone-building action of real progesterone."

Projects:

1. Make a poster of the chart shown on page 100 of the text, regarding the effects of contraceptive medication.

2. Write a book review of Kippley's *The Art of Natural Family Planning* or *Sex and the Marriage Covenant*, or Janet Smith's *Humanae Vitae: A Generation Later*.

3. Ask your pastor or Pre-Cana team to include a segment on Natural Family Planning in marriage-preparation programs.

References:

Catechism of the Catholic Church
Clowes, Brian. *The Facts of Life*
Drummey, James J. *Catholic Replies*
Flannery, Austin, O.P. *Vatican Council II: The Conciliar and Post Conciliar Documents*
Grisez, Germain. *Christian Moral Principles*
_____. *Difficult Moral Questions*
_____. *Living a Christian Life*
Hardon, John A., S.J. *The Catholic Catechism*
_____. *Modern Catholic Dictionary*
_____. *The Question and Answer Catholic Catechism*
Hayes, Edward J., Hayes, Paul J. and Drummey, James J. *Catholicism and Life*
_____. *Catholicism and Reason*
_____. *Catholicism and Society*
John Paul II, Pope. *Evangelium Vitae* ("The Gospel of Life")
_____. *Familiaris Consortio* ("The Role of the Christian Family in the Modern World")
_____. *Veritatis Splendor* ("The Splendor of Truth")
Kippley, John. *Sex and the Marriage Covenant*
_____. and Kippley, Sheila. *The Art of Natural Family Planning*
May, William E. *An Introduction to Moral Theology*
Paul VI, Pope. *Humanae Vitae* ("On Human Life")
Pius XI, Pope. "On Christian Marriage" (*Casti Connubii*)
Smith, Janet E. *Humanae Vitae: A Generation Later*
Vatican II. *Gaudium et Spes* ("Pastoral Constitution on the Church in the Modern World")
Wuerl, Donald, Lawler, Thomas and Lawler, Ronald. *The Catholic Catechism*
_____. *The Teaching of Christ*

Manipulating Human Life

Purpose: The purpose of this lesson is to show the moral and ethical problems that stem from such "Brave New World" experimentation on human life as cloning, in vitro fertilization, artificial insemination, and the use of fertility drugs.

Tips for Teachers: You could stimulate discussion by assigning Aldous Huxley's book *Brave New World* or showing excerpts from the movie based on the book. Just the first part of the book or movie, which deals with creation of life in the laboratory, would be sufficient to make the point that what Huxley saw as science fiction back in the 1930s has become a frightening reality today. Robin Cook's work of fiction, *Coma*, and the movie of the same name, also illustrate the dangers of manipulating human life.

Discussion could also be started by asking the students for their opinion of cloning, "test tube" babies, and artificial insemination. Why can't these technologies be used when so many couples are childless and unable to have children the normal way? The answers to that question can be found in *Donum Vitae*, the Vatican's "Instruction on Respect for Human Life in Its Origins and on the Dignity of Procreation." You can refer to the excerpts from this document that are in the text or, if the students are bright enough, perhaps get copies of the document for them to discuss in detail.

In taking up each of the immoral technologies being promoted today, start with cloning and spell out what the cloning process involves (how many failures there were before "Dolly" was successfully cloned). Cardinal O'Connor's remarks are very important in offering solid reasons for opposing cloning, and the catechist must continually make the point that just because something is technically possible doesn't make it morally right.

The next topic is in vitro fertilization. Note that the success rate is about 25 percent and then discuss what happens to the failures. What seems on the surface to be a wonderful scientific advance has an ugly side that includes destruction of human embryos, experimentation on them, and freezing them for future implantation. There are already court battles over who owns these thousands of tiny human beings and whether and when they should be destroyed. This is what happens when scientists try to play God.

Donum Vitae and Pope John Paul (cf. pages 109-110 of the text) give us reasons for opposing this manipulation and such related immoral activities as surrogate motherhood.

Review carefully the section on artificial insemination, making clear to the class what is involved and explaining why the only morally permissible method is assisted insemination, provided that the sperm is not obtained by masturbation and that the method is used to promote fertilization for a married couple once natural intercourse has taken place.

Also to be covered are prenatal testing methods, such as amniocentesis and ultrasound, which are moral if carried out to determine a medical treatment for a child in the womb, but are immoral if used to justify abortion.

The use of fertility drugs leads to the possibility of multiple births, and couples must be aware of this and be prepared to care for however many children may be born. The birth of septuplets to the McCaughey family in 1999, following the refusal of the parents to have any of the children aborted during pregnancy, and their willingness to choose life for all their children show a strong faith in God. Some of the students should look up the details of this story in connection with this lesson.

The final component of this lesson, and a very important component, concerns the compassion that the Church has for childless couples (cf. *Donum Vitae*, Part II, 8). Children must be the fruit of their parents' love and not the product of laboratory science. So however heart-wrenching childlessness is, one cannot employ immoral means to overcome it, or much more serious problems will arise.

Topics for Discussion:

1. Should everything that is scientifically possible be tried in the laboratory?

2. What is the ethical difference between "having a child" and "making a child"?

3. Is surrogate motherhood a good thing?

4. What would your reaction be if your parents told you
that you had been cloned?

5. What is wrong with same-sex couples using artificial
insemination to bring children into the world?

Some Questions and Answers:

**1. Is a Catholic couple excommunicated if they have
a child via in vitro fertilization, and can such a child
be baptized in the Catholic Church?**

A. No to the first question and yes to the second. Conceiving a child through IVF is immoral, according to Catholic teaching, but there is no penalty of excommunication attached. The
child resulting from this process, said *Donum Vitae*, "must in
any case be accepted as a living gift of the divine Goodness
and must be brought up with love" (Part II, B5).

**2. But doesn't the Church care about couples who
want children but are unable to have them in the usual
way?**

A. Of course the Church cares. She is after all both our
Mother and our Teacher (*Mater et Magistra*). But the Church
insists that "the act of conjugal love is ... the only setting wor-
thy of human procreation." It teaches that the conception of
life in the laboratory and transfer of the new life to the womb
of the mother is "illicit and in opposition to the dignity of procreation and of the conjugal union, even when everything is
done to avoid the death of the human embryo" (*Donum Vitae*,
Part II, B5).

The Church believes that the child conceived "must be the
fruit of his parents' love. He cannot be desired or conceived as
the product of an intervention of medical or biological techniques; that would be equivalent to reducing him to an object
of scientific technology" (Part II, B4).

**3. I saw a movie on television called *Labor of Love*.
It was about a grandmother who acted as a surrogate
mother for her daughter's baby. All the grandmother
did was hold her grandchild inside her for nine months.
What's wrong with that?**

A. The Church has condemned surrogate motherhood because "it is contrary to the unity of marriage and to the dignity of the procreation of the human person." The Church teaches that "marriage does not confer on the spouses the right to have a child, but only the right to perform those natural acts which are per se ordered to procreation."

Donum Vitae also says that "a true and proper right to a child would be contrary to the child's dignity and nature. The child is not an object to which one has a right, nor can he be considered as an object of ownership: rather, a child is a gift, 'the supreme gift' and the most gratuitous gift of marriage, and is a living testimony of the mutual giving of his parents. For this reason, the child has the right, as already mentioned, to be the fruit of the specific act of the conjugal love of his parents; and he also has the right to be respected as a person from the moment of his conception" (Part II, B8).

4. What are some of the ethical problems associated with cloning human beings?

A. It is interesting to note that Ian Wilmut, the Scottish scientist who cloned Dolly the sheep in 1997, has since then spoken out sharply against the idea of trying to clone a human. "You have to be sick to even suggest it," Wilmut said at a symposium on cloning in June 1999. "In my view, it is not in the interest of the child." He said that while he would favor the use of cloning for genetic modifications that could eliminate disease, he would oppose using this new technology to produce "improved" children.

"I'm not sure where the line is," said Wilmut, "but I think there is a line. I don't like the idea of enhancement. Why can't we accept our children as they are?"

As for the ethical problems, one good place to look for a summary of them is the statement issued by the Pontifical Academy for Life on June 25, 1997. The text can be found in the May 21, 1998 issue of *Origins*, the weekly publication of the Catholic News Service in Washington, DC.

Among other things, the Pontifical Academy said:

> In the cloning process the basic relationships of the human person are perverted: filiation, consanguinity, kinship, parenthood. A woman can be the twin sister of her mother,

lack a biological father, and be the daughter of her grand-father. In vitro fertilization has already led to the confusion of parentage, but cloning will mean the radical rupture of these bonds.

The Academy also said that "the 'human cloning' project represents the terrible aberration to which value-free science is driven and is a sign of the profound malaise of our civilization, which looks to science, technology, and the 'quality of life' as surrogates for the meaning of life and its salvation."

Projects:

1. Clip three articles from newspapers or magazines about the use of the technologies discussed in this lesson.
2. Write a review of the movie *Brave New World* or the movie *Coma.*
3. Make a poster listing the major problems of cloning.
4. Make a poster listing the key points in *Donum Vitae.*

References:

Catechism of the Catholic Church
Clowes, Brian. *The Facts of Life*
Drummey, James J. *Catholic Replies*
Grisez, Germain. *Christian Moral Principles*
_____. *Difficult Moral Questions*
_____. *Living a Christian Life*
Hardon, John A., S.J. *The Catholic Catechism*
Hayes, Edward J., Hayes, Paul J. and Drummey, James J.
    Catholicism and Life
_____. *Catholicism and Society*
John Paul II, Pope. *Evangelium Vitae* ("The Gospel of Life")
Paul VI, Pope. *Humanae Vitae* ("On Human Life")
Pontifical Academy for Life. *Reflections on Cloning*
Rini, Suzanne. *Beyond Abortion: A Chronicle of Fetal Experimentation*
Sacred Congregation for the Doctrine of the Faith. *Donum Vitae* ("Instruction on Respect for Human Life in Its Origins and on the Dignity of Procreation")

The Destruction of Life

Purpose: The purpose of this lesson is to show that the culture of death has replaced the culture of life, that our right to life comes from God, and that direct abortion is a horrendous crime.

Tips for Teachers: There are many good books, videos, and speakers about the development of human life and abortion procedures, as well as about women and doctors victimized by abortion who became pro-life. These resources should be available through your diocesan pro-life office or through local pro-life groups, and catechists and group leaders should take advantage of these materials.

The topic could also be introduced with current examples from the media of the pervasiveness of what Pope John Paul called the "culture of death." It is important to point out that this contempt for innocent human life is contrary not only to the Bible and to Christian moral principles, but also to a secular document like the Declaration of Independence.

It would be good to review Thomas Jefferson's words about every person being endowed by their Creator with certain inalienable rights, the chief of which is the right to life. Note that if that primary right is not safeguarded, none of our other rights will matter.

Pope John Paul spoke very forcefully about the evil of abortion in *Evangelium Vitae*, his encyclical on "The Gospel of Life," and that document ought to be an integral part of this and subsequent lessons. The teacher should also show the parallels between Hitler's Holocaust against the Jewish people and the "Silent Holocaust" of abortion, using Professor William Brennan's book *The Abortion Holocaust* for documentation.

Having done this groundwork, the catechist or group leader can then get into a precise definition of abortion and make the distinction between spontaneous abortion (miscarriage), indirect abortion, and direct abortion. As unpleasant as they are, the various methods of abortion need to be described, especially the horrific technique known as "partial-birth abortion" (cf. pp. 130-

131 of the text). Point out the hypocrisy of a media that refuse to show this barbaric method of killing, allegedly because it would offend the sensibilities of readers and watchers, but at the same time show gruesome pictures of those victimized by war and natural disasters.

Prayer vigils, rosary processions, and marches for life are good activities in which to involve young people. Here are some general intercessions that could be used at Mass or as part of a prayer service:

— That the Church, the People of Life, may bear joyful witness that each human life comes from God, belongs to God, and is meant to return to God, we pray to the Lord.

— That the Church, called to a preferential option for the poor, may always speak up for the unborn child, the most defenseless of God's children, we pray to the Lord.

— That children still on their way to birth may be welcomed and protected rather than feared and rejected, we pray to the Lord.

— That mothers who are pregnant but afraid of their motherhood may, with the help of the Church, find the courage and strength they need to give life, we pray to the Lord.

— That those who are tempted to have their children aborted may find in the Christian community the wisdom and resources to protect the new lives that have been entrusted to them, we pray to the Lord.

— That Almighty God, the Author of all life, will enlighten the minds and change the hearts of all those who favor, promote, seek, or perform abortions, we pray to the Lord.

Topics for Discussion:

1. Comment on this statement: "God alone is the Lord of life from its beginning until its end; no one can under any

circumstances claim for himself the right directly to destroy an innocent human life" (*Catechism*, n. 2258).

2. Comment on this statement from the Declaration of Independence: "We hold these truths to be self-evident, that all men are created equal, that they are endowed by their Creator with certain inalienable rights, that among these are life, liberty, and the pursuit of happiness."

3. How can we carry out this command of Pope John Paul: "Respect, protect, love, and serve life, every human life!" (*Evangelium Vitae*, n. 5)?

4. How can doctors who are trained to be curers become instead killers of their most vulnerable patients?

Some Questions and Answers:

1. Is it true that the Catholic Church at one time in history permitted abortion?

A. No, it is not true. The Catholic Church has for two thousand years taught that abortion is always and everywhere evil. Way back in the first century, in a book of apostolic teachings called the *Didache*, the Church told the faithful: "You shall not procure abortion. You shall not destroy a newborn child."

This condemnation was repeated many times through the centuries by saints and Popes, and was reaffirmed by the Second Vatican Council (1962-1965), which called abortion an "unspeakable crime." The Catholic Bishops of the United States have also denounced the "moral evil of abortion" and have stated that "no Catholic can responsibly take a 'pro-choice' stand when the 'choice' in question involves the taking of innocent human life."

And Pope John Paul II, in *Evangelium Vitae*, used his full authority as the Vicar of Christ on earth to declare that "direct abortion, that is, abortion willed as an end or as a means, always constitutes a grave moral disorder since it is the deliberate killing of an innocent human being" (n. 62).

2. "But if we pass laws forbidding abortion," a friend says, **"thousands of women will be forced to put their lives in the hands of back-alley butchers." Please respond to this.**

A. This statement is based on two assumptions: that thousands of women died from illegal abortion prior to its legalization in the United States in 1973, and that illegal abortions are reduced when abortion becomes lawful. Both assumptions are false. In 1973, the year the U.S. Supreme Court struck down all laws against abortion, only 45 women died from illegal abortions, not the "thousands" claimed by the pro-abortionists. But since 1973, scores of women have died from so-called safe, legal abortions, and they will continue to die, and to suffer severe physical and mental complications, because abortion can be a dangerous medical procedure even when performed in an accredited hospital or a licensed clinic.

Second, legalization of abortion does not put an end to illegal procedures. They continue in large numbers because there are several situations where a woman might prefer an illegal abortion. For instance, a married woman who becomes pregnant by another man, or the teenage daughter of a public official, or a woman who does not have the money or the desire to go through the red tape at the local hospital. Thus, even where legal abortions are easily available, there are some women who will still seek illegal ones and suffer the tragic consequences in order to conceal their pregnancy.

And isn't it silly to argue that the best way to prevent the illegal killing of unborn babies is to make it legal to kill them? By the same logic, we can stop such illegal actions as murder, bank robbery, and car theft by making it legal to murder, rob banks, and steal cars.

3. An editorial in a newspaper says that abortion is a Catholic issue and that Catholics have no right to force their moral views on others. How would you respond to this editorial?

A. First of all, abortion is not a Catholic issue; it is a human rights and a civil rights issue that is of great concern to people of all religious faiths and those of none. As citizens, Catholics have just as much right as anyone else to state their views on public issues, especially on a matter of such grave consequence as the preservation of innocent human life.

But the more important fallacy is the absurd notion that no one should try to impose his moral views on anyone else. Is not this newspaper imposing its moral view on those who are opposed to abortion? Does not virtually every law on our books impose a moral view on someone—on murderers, rapists, thieves, drug pushers?

If this logic were carried to its natural conclusion, you would be expected to watch your next-door neighbor drowning his child in a swimming pool and not do anything about it because you would be accused of forcing your moral views on him. Catholics and others who value human life had better try to persuade a majority of the American people to oppose abortion and euthanasia or no one's life will be safe.

4. Is abortion allowed to save the mother's life?

A. No, the Catholic Church does not permit the direct and intentional killing of an unborn baby for any reason. If the mother's life is in danger, the Church expects the doctor to do everything possible to save the mother and the baby.

But if you are talking about *indirect* abortion, e.g., removing a cancerous uterus to save the mother's life, knowing that the operation will cause the death of the child growing inside that uterus, that is morally permissible under the principle of the double effect since the death of the child is not directly willed, but is rather the unintended side effect of a legitimate medical procedure.

Projects:

1. Make pro-life banners and posters.

2. Conduct a prayer service for life.

3. Bring in newspaper and magazine clippings showing that we live in a "culture of death."

4. Bring in newspaper and magazine clippings showing signs of a "culture of life."

5. Volunteer to help your parish or community pro-life group.

6. Organize a baby shower for those mothers faced with problem pregnancies who have decided to have their babies.

7. Ask your pastor to include at Mass some of the general intercessions mentioned on page 88 of this manual.

8. Arrange for pro-life speakers or videos at your school or parish.

References:

Alcorn, Randy. *Pro-Life Answers to Pro-Choice Arguments*
Brennan, William. *The Abortion Holocaust*
Catechism of the Catholic Church
DeMarco, Donald. *Biotechnology and the Assault on Parenthood*
Everett, Carol. *Blood Money: Getting Rich off a Woman's Right to Choose*
John Paul II, Pope. *Evangelium Vitae* ("The Gospel of Life")
Lawler, Ronald, Boyle, Joseph, and May, William. *Catholic Sexual Ethics*
Myers, Bishop John J. *The Obligations of Catholics and the Rights of Unborn Children*
Nathanson, Bernard N., M.D. *Aborting America*
_____. *The Hand of God*
O'Connor, John Cardinal. *Abortion: Questions and Answers*
Paul VI, Pope. *Humanae Vitae* ("On Human Life")
Reardon, David. *Aborted Women: Silent No More*
Rice, Charles E. *50 Questions on Abortion, Euthanasia and Related Issues*
_____. *No Exception: A Pro-Life Imperative*
Sacred Congregation for the Doctrine of the Faith. *Declaration on Procured Abortion*
Smith, Herbert F., S.J. *Pro-Choice? Pro-Life?*
Willke, Dr. and Mrs. J. C. *Abortion Questions and Answers*

Abortion Penalties and Compassion

Purpose: The purpose of this lesson is to show the Church's modern condemnations of abortion and the penalties attached, demonstrate that there are no valid reasons to justify abortion, and stress the need for compassion for the victims.

Tips for Teachers: Begin by reviewing the Church's condemnation of abortion in recent decades, including the very strong, and possibly infallible, statement of Pope John Paul in *Evangelium Vitae* (cf. page 129 of the text). The material under "Some Questions and Answers," both in the previous lesson and in this lesson, will be helpful.

In discussing the penalty of excommunication that the Church has attached to abortion, make sure to go over the conditions required for excommunication. A person who is ignorant of this penalty, is under the age of 16, thinks that the law applies only to the one having the abortion and not to her accomplices, or sincerely believes abortion is necessary and permissible to preserve the mother's life would not automatically incur excommunication.

Bring up the reasons usually offered to justify abortion and provide the answers to them, either from this manual, from the text, or from some of the references cited (see also pages 96-101 of *Catholicism and Society*, a companion volume in this series). And don't forget to mention that adoption is a good alternative to abortion.

It is also important to mention the lies that are told by the pro-abortion side not only to women and young girls who seek abortions, but also to the population at large, especially with regard to the deaths and serious complications that follow many so-called safe, legal abortions. The books by David Reardon and Carol Everett (she once operated two abortion chambers) will be helpful here.

Emphasize that it is not enough to be anti-abortion, one must be pro-life, i.e., one must hate the sin but love the sinner and show compassion for the women who have been victimized by the promoters of this horrendous crime. Have the class get involved with a local Pregnancy Help, Birthright, Care Net, or Project Rachel group, organizing baby showers, holding prayer vigils or Eucharistic adoration, or giving whatever support is necessary for those facing crisis pregnancies.

The final segment in this lesson deals with baptism of a baby and the morality of induction of labor.

Topics for Discussion:

1. Give some examples of the culture of death.

2. Why must all human life be protected from the womb to the tomb?

3. How would you answer someone who says that we should not help a woman who has had an abortion because she made the evil choice herself and doesn't deserve any help?

4. Are those politicians who vote to keep abortion legal automatically excommunicated?

Some Questions and Answers:

1. Is there a connection between abortion and breast cancer?

A. Twenty-five out of 31 epidemiologic studies on women of African, Asian, and European ancestry have found that even one abortion increases the risk of getting breast cancer later in life. In the fall of 1998, the World Conference on Breast Cancer published its *Global Action Plan Report*. Under the subject of risk factors related to hormones, the *Report* reads:

> Today, women in general are exposed to higher levels of estrogen during their lifetime than was the case in previous generations. It is believed that women now face excess levels of both natural and synthetic estrogens, increasing their risk of breast cancer. Prolonged use of the birth control pills, late or lack of pregnancies and breast-feeding, **induced termination of pregnancies**, a diet high in fat, meat, or dairy products, and hormone replacement therapy following menopause, all are cited as risk factors for increased estrogens and breast cancer.

2. Why can't a person be "pro-choice" and a Catholic in good standing?

A. Because the Catholic Church has condemned abortion as an "unspeakable crime" and because the "choice" this person is advocating will result in a dead baby, and no one should have the right to choose to kill another human being because that human being's existence is inconvenient to them. It would be like saying that the pusher selling deadly drugs to children is not really pro-drugs, but only pro-choice; he is simply in favor of giving children the choice of whether or not to use drugs.

In their 1998 statement *Living the Gospel of Life*, the Catholic Bishops of the United States said that the basic principle is simple:

> We must begin with a commitment never to intentionally kill, or collude in the killing of, any innocent human life, no matter how broken, unformed, disabled, or desperate that life may seem. In other words, the choice of certain ways of acting is always and radically incompatible with the love of God and the dignity of the human person created in his image.
>
> Direct abortion is never a morally tolerable option. It is always a grave act of violence against a woman and her unborn child. This is so even when the woman does not see the truth because of the pressures she may be subjected to, often by the child's father, her parents, or friends (n. 21).

Catholics must also be very careful not to use the language of those promoting abortion since their words and phrases are designed to conceal what is really happening. Thus, we say "baby," not "fetus." We say "pro-abortion," not "pro-choice." We say "killing an unborn child," not "terminating a pregnancy." We say "pro-life," not "anti-abortion."

3. Is it a sin to vote for a political candidate who is pro-abortion?

A. Any Catholic who votes for a political candidate *because* he is for abortion is objectively guilty of a gravely immoral action. If that Catholic sufficiently understands what he is doing, and fully consents to it, he has committed a mortal sin that must be confessed in the sacrament of Penance.

In his 1990 pastoral letter on *The Obligations of Catholics and the Rights of Unborn Children,* Bishop John Myers of Peoria, Illinois said that those who assist candidates for public office "because of their position on abortion are guilty of complicity in the abortions their election would make possible." He said that "one is formally complicit in the injustice of abortion when one votes for a candidate even partially on the basis of his or her pro-abortion position."

As for those Catholic officials who support abortion, the U.S. Bishops, in their 1998 statement *Living the Gospel of Life,* asked these officials "to consider the consequences for their own spiritual well-being, as well as the scandal they risk by leading others into serious sin. We call on them to reflect on the grave contradiction of assuming public roles and presenting themselves as credible Catholics when their actions on fundamental issues of human life are not in agreement with Church teaching."

The American Bishops said that "no public official, especially one claiming to be a faithful and serious Catholic, can responsibly advocate for or actively support direct attacks on innocent human life" (n. 32).

4. Can you prove that having an abortion in a licensed facility is not always a safe procedure?

A. The proof can be found in books such as David Reardon's *Aborted Women: Silent No More* and Carol Everett's *Blood Money: Getting Rich off a Woman's Right to Choose.* There was also a revealing interview in the January 1999 issue of *Catholic World Report* with Eric Harrah, who was once the owner of a chain of 13 abortion factories.

Among other things, Harrah, who is now pro-life, said that "we had doctors who were just overworked and tired, doing uterine perforations, cervical tears, and things like that. I've seen everything: doctors who would rip out ovaries, or puncture the uterine wall, or end up with intestines in their hands" (p. 45).

He said that there was never a successful lawsuit for a

botched abortion against his facilities because he and his partners forced the women coming to them to sign 30-page consent forms. "These women basically signed their lives away," he said. "They signed away every legal right they ever had."

Harrah also said that if a woman threatened a malpractice suit, all he had to say to scare her away was, "Sweetheart, take me to court. What are all your friends and family going to think when your name comes up in the newspaper, suing because you had an abortion that didn't go the way you thought it should go?" (*Ibid.*)

Projects:

1. Bring in clippings from newspapers and magazines that show Catholic politicians taking a pro-abortion position.

2. Pray the rosary outside an abortion factory.

3. Arrange for a pro-life speaker or video in your school or parish.

4. Hold a pro-life prayer vigil for an end to the abortion holocaust.

5. Volunteer to help at one of the more than 3,000 crisis pregnancy centers in the United States.

References:

Alcorn, Randy. *Pro-Life Answers to Pro-Choice Arguments*
Brennan, William. *The Abortion Holocaust*
Everett, Carol. *Blood Money: Getting Rich off a Woman's Right to Choose*
John Paul II, Pope. *Evangelium Vitae* ("The Gospel of Life")
Myers, Bishop John J. *The Obligations of Catholics and the Rights of Unborn Children*
Nathanson, Bernard N., M.D. *Aborting America*
_____. *The Hand of God*
O'Connor, John Cardinal. *Abortion: Questions and Answers*
Paul VI, Pope. *Humanae Vitae* ("On Human Life")
Reardon, David. *Aborted Women: Silent No More*
Sacred Congregation for the Doctrine of the Faith. *Declaration on Procured Abortion*
Smith, Herbert F., S.J. *Pro-Choice? Pro-Life?*
Willke, Dr. and Mrs. J. C. *Abortion Questions and Answers*

Euthanasia and Assisted Suicide

Purpose: The purpose of this lesson is to show that euthanasia and assisted suicide are grave evils and to explain the nature and importance of advance medical directives or health-care proxies.

Tips for Teachers: Since end-of-life issues are constantly in the news, the catechist could begin this lesson by going over stories from the media that the students had been asked ahead of time to bring to class. Spend time analyzing the arguments given in favor of killing the old and the sick directly, as well as helping them to kill themselves through "assisted suicide," and then explain why this so-called mercy killing is wrong. Discuss in detail the ten arguments against euthanasia on page 136 of the text and ask which is the most convincing or the most important to each of the students.

The statements of Pope John Paul, especially his pronouncement in *Evangelium Vitae* that "euthanasia is a grave violation of the law of God," are very important for any Catholic who wants to know how to address these issues in the right way. The chart on page 137 of the text will be helpful in distinguishing between moral and immoral ways of caring for the terminally ill.

It would be a good idea for the teacher of high school, college, or nursing students to schedule a visit to a chronic-care hospital, a hospice, a nursing home, or some other health-care facility to get an idea of the problems faced by the elderly and the sick — and by those who care for them. The students could also write letters to some of the residents of these places, or visit them frequently, reading to them, helping them to write letters, or just providing them with companionship since some of them have no families and are often lonely.

Another important subject is the matter of pain management. "Kill the pain, not the patient" should be our slogan. There is no reason for a person to endure terrible suffering when it is perfectly moral to administer narcotics to the dying, as both Popes Pius XII and John Paul II have explained (cf. pages 139-141 of the text). The use of drugs is permitted under Catholic teaching, even if the patient's life would be shortened. According to the principle of the double effect, this is allowable because the intention is not to kill the patient but to relieve his pain. Control of pain and suffering would eliminate the demand for assisted suicide.

Because some persons may not be competent to make medical decisions near the end of life, it is essential that they have signed an advanced medical directive that would leave these decisions up to trustworthy agents who know the patient's wishes and who will see that they are carried out. Merely signing a piece of paper, such as a living will, is not enough for the reasons mentioned on page 142 of the text. The catechist or group leader should point out the advantages of a durable power of attorney or health care proxy, and then review the four conditions that would necessitate the use of an advance medical directive.

Finally, spend some time going over the "Christian Affirmation of Life" and the sample health care proxy, noting that both revolve around recognition of the dignity of each person and our eternal destiny with God.

Also helpful with this lesson will be the material on ordinary vs. extraordinary means on pages 50-53 of this manual, the material on artificial nutrition and hydration on pages 158-162 of the text, as well as the *Declaration on Euthanasia, Evangelium Vitae*, the *Charter for Health Care Workers*, and Wesley Smith's book *Forced Exit*.

Topics for Discussion:

1. What is the Catholic understanding of the statement that everyone should be able to die with dignity?

2. How would you answer someone who says that euthanasia and physician-assisted suicide are needed today to relieve families and societies of financial burdens?

3. Doctors are obligated to preserve life, not end it.

4. Can legal permission to die become a duty to die?

5. What did Pope John Paul mean when he referred to euthanasia as a "false mercy"?

6. What are some of the problems with living wills?

7. What are some of the advantages of advance medical directives?

Some Questions and Answers:

1. Is there an effective way to discuss the subject of euthanasia?

A. Fr. Robert Spitzer, S.J., president of Gonzaga University in Washington and author of a new book and training program called *Life Principles*, is an authority on euthanasia. Although he was asked specifically how priests could speak about the topic to their congregations, his answer in the publication *Priests for Life* will be of help to any Catholic:

> When we talk about euthanasia and assisted suicide, we must include three fundamental points that are of premium importance to most people. First, there is the terrifying subject of *pain*. We cannot be afraid to tackle this question head-on. We have to get across that (a) 96 percent of all pain can be 100 percent controlled with modern-day medications; (b) nearly 100 percent of suicide requests from patients are reversed the moment pain and depression are treated; and (c) most types of pain medication and treatments can be administered *in the home*. Patients need not be afraid that they will have to be locked up in hospitals for long periods of time in order to obtain pain treatment.

> The second area to look at is *quality of life*. People need to ask themselves: "What makes my life worth living?" I often tell them that there are four different ways of evaluating one's quality of life — four different levels, if you will. Level One is based on *autonomy*, Level Two is based on *pleasure*, Level Three on *love*, and Level Four on *faith*.

> If we define our life in terms of Levels One and Two, we are headed for a lot of trouble because we must all necessarily endure suffering and a loss of autonomy. However, if we evaluate our life based on Levels Three and Four, we can always be happy, no matter how much suffering we go through. When our life's worth is determined by love, family, wisdom, friends, work, faith, and God, a grandmother of 90 can do just as well and better than a 30-year-old. It is essential for us to help people define

the quality of their lives *before* terrible things begin to happen to them.

Finally, we have to address the question most often hurled at pro-lifers: "Who are you to tell me what to do?" Our response should be that we do not relish giving people directives. Rather, they are the ones who are opening up a can of worms by pushing to make euthanasia legal. Giving people more options is not always best. In this case, more options will end up being more burdensome to society than freeing.

Projects:

1. Volunteer at a hospital, hospice, or nursing home.

2. Organize a group to help elderly persons in your neighborhood with such things as chores, shopping, doctor's visits, Mass attendance, etc.

3. Enlist the help of the elderly with tutoring, projects for school or parish, and letter-writing campaigns to legislators on life issues.

4. Invite a senior citizen to speak to the class.

5. Organize the celebration of the Anointing of the Sick at your parish church and arrange for transportation to get the old and the sick to the service.

References:

Catechism of the Catholic Church
John Paul II, Pope. *Evangelium Vitae* ("The Gospel of Life")
_____. *Salvifici Doloris* ("On the Christian Meaning of Suffering")
Kreeft, Peter. *Making Sense Out of Suffering*
Paul VI, Pope. *Humanae Vitae* ("On Human Life")
Pontifical Council for Pastoral Assistance. *Charter for Health Care Workers*
Sacred Congregation for the Doctrine of the Faith. *Declaration on Euthanasia*
Smith, Wesley J. *Forced Exit*

Mutilation and Sterilization

Purpose: The purpose of this lesson is to show the conditions that permit mutilation of the body, the reasons why direct sterilization is immoral, and the morality of plastic surgery and organ donation.

Tips for Teachers: Ask for examples of what steps we may take to preserve our life and health. Show the difference between mutilation that is morally okay and that which is not, recalling the principle of totality from page 66 of the text. Since the whole of the body is greater than any of its parts, a diseased organ may be removed for the good of the whole body, and even a healthy organ can be removed under certain conditions (see the examples in the text).

One very common way of preventing conception of babies today is sterilization, either of males (vasectomy) or females (tubal ligation). If the operation is directly intended to make reproduction impossible, it is immoral. If the sterilizing effects are an indirect consequence of surgery necessary to preserve a person's life or health, then it is permissible under the principle of the twofold effect. Direct sterilization, of course, is forbidden in Catholic hospitals.

A related category is that of plastic surgery, which also has moral implications in some situations. Spell out the conditions under which it is right and when it would be wrong.

Finally, there is the complicated area of tissue and organ transplants and donations. The charts on pages 165 and 166 of the text will be useful in illustrating the different kinds of transplants, whether they constitute major or minor mutilation, and the conditions under which they are permissible. As in so many of these life issues, doctors and scientists have crossed into once unimaginable territory, such as "harvesting" the organs of aborted babies to treat adult diseases and taking organs from people who are still alive.

Tissue and organ donation can be a good and praiseworthy

thing, as Pope John Paul and the *Catechism* pointed out, but make sure that the students understand the moral strictures that must be in place in order to protect the dignity of the human person and the functional integrity of the human body.

Topics for Discussion:

1. What steps are we permitted to take to preserve our life and health?

2. Is it ever right to mutilate our bodies?

3. Should persons convicted of crimes be sterilized?

4. Should persons who might have children with defects be sterilized?

5. Is plastic surgery always permitted?

6. Is it all right to take an organ from a person not quite dead since he's going to die anyway and the organ would be fresher?

Some Questions and Answers:

1. Is there really a problem with body piercing?

A. According to medical people, it is a health hazard to pierce one's lips, cheeks, tongue, or other body parts. Dr. Sheila Price, professor at the West Virginia University School of Dentistry, says that the risks of such piercing include possible transmission of hepatitis, HIV, and other blood-borne pathogens. Also concerned is Dr. Timothy Rose, the president of the American Dental Association, who says that "to have a needle — clean or dirty — stuck through a vascular part of your body in that way, the risk of diseases has to be immense, and there can be nerve damage that affects the way you talk and swallow."

2. What is all this discussion about stem cell research?

A. Researchers at two American universities reported in November 1998 that they had discovered ways to use human embryonic stem cells to treat various diseases and bring about bodily healing. The stem cells have been described as master cells that have the potential to develop into different kinds of cells needed to produce the various parts of the body. The problem is that advocates of this research want to harvest the cells from living human embryos, which of course would kill the embryos.

Speaking for the U.S. Bishops, Richard Doerflinger told the National Bioethics Advisory Commission that "from the time of the Nuremberg Code, ethical norms on human experimentation have demanded that we never inflict death or disabling injury on any unconsenting individual of the human species simply for the sake of benefit to others. Stem cell research requiring the destructive harvesting of cells from living embryos fails this test and should not be supported by the government."

Some scientists have advocated the use of cloning to produce embryos genetically identical to each individual patient. Each time a patient needs a transplant, he or she will donate some body cells, which will be used to make numerous embryonic twin brothers or sisters — who will then be killed for their own cells.

But there is no need to go down that road, says Doerflinger, since "genetically compatible tissue for transplantation can be produced by using and adapting patients' own adult stem cells. These are now known to be far more versatile than was once imagined — and they pose no serious moral problem."

Projects:

1. Make posters of the charts on pages 165 and 166 of the text and give a short explanation of each chart.

2. Interview someone with an organ donor card and ask them why they want to be an organ donor.

3. Interview someone with pierced body parts and ask if they have considered the health hazards involved.

References:

Catechism of the Catholic Church
Grisez, Germain. *Living a Christian Life*
John Paul II, Pope. *Evangelium Vitae* ("The Gospel of Life")
Kippley, John. *Sex and the Marriage Covenant*
Lawler, Ronald, Boyle, Joseph and May, William E. *Catholic Sexual Ethics*

Artificial Nutrition and Hydration

Purpose: The purpose of this lesson is to spell out the principles involved in continuing or discontinuing artificial nutrition and hydration and to demonstrate how to apply these principles to specific cases.

Tips for Teachers: Since this lesson is related to Lesson 18, it can be discussed in conjunction with that lesson and with the material on ordinary vs. extraordinary means in chapter five of the text (Lesson 8). After briefly reviewing the key points of those two lessons, the catechist or group leader ought to go over the basic moral principles mentioned on pages 159-160 of the text and then take up the topic of artificial nutrition and hydration (ANH).

Reference to the *Catechism of the Catholic Church*, the *Declaration on Euthanasia*, the *Charter for Health Care Workers*, Wesley Smith's book *Forced Exit*, and the information about the Hugh Finn case in "Some Questions and Answers" will help in preparing and teaching this lesson.

Make sure that the class understands the precise meaning of ANH and then set forth the arguments presented by both sides. A key point to be stressed is that ANH is *not* medical care — it does not cure any disease — but is rather the provision of the basic necessities of food and water. Withdrawing them is not humane if it is meant to terminate a life.

Take the specific cases mentioned on pages 161-162 of the text, along with the Hugh Finn case, and show how the principles should be applied. The bottom line is that ANH should be provided unless it is clearly useless because the dying process has begun and cannot be reversed and it would only constitute an unreasonable burden to the patient.

Emphasize Pope John Paul's statement in *Evangelium Vitae* (n. 65) that forgoing disproportionate means of medical care is not equivalent to suicide or euthanasia, but is rather "acceptance of the human condition in the face of death."

Topics for Discussion:

1. Is it ever morally right to withdraw artificial nutrition and hydration?
2. What are the basic moral principles that ought to enter into life and death decisions?
3. Do people sometimes come out of longtime comas?

Some Questions and Answers:

1. A Virginia man named Hugh Finn was left comatose after an automobile accident. He died three years later after doctors removed a tube that had provided him with food and water. A Virginia court had ruled that "withdrawal of artificial nutrition or hydration from Hugh Finn, a person in a persistent vegetative state, merely permits the natural process of dying and is not mercy killing or euthanasia." Is that true?

A. No, it is not true. Reliable Catholic moralists hold that food and water are not primarily forms of medical treatment because of and by themselves they do not overcome disease or restore health. Rather, they are basic means of sustaining life, and a person who is not imminently dying will certainly die without them. Thus, nutrition and hydration should be provided as part of a patient's normal care, unless or until the benefits of such care are clearly useless in sustaining life or pose a definite danger or burden to the patient.

Hugh Finn was in an unconscious but non-dying condition. Taking food and water away from him did not "merely permit the natural process of dying," but rather hastened his death by starvation and dehydration. If the withdrawal of nutrition and hydration were intended to hasten or cause his death, then it was euthanasia, and that is not permitted by Catholic teaching.

The Church holds that nutrition and hydration should be supplied to an unconscious, non-dying patient. Such feeding is not useless because it keeps the patient alive. It was morally wrong to withdraw food and water from Hugh Finn because there was no indication that he was suffering or that food and water were an unreasonable danger or burden to him.

2. When my aunt was in the last stages of terminal cancer, a hospice worker advised us to disconnect the feeding and hydration tube as a "humane" way of ending her suffering in a matter of a few days. She told us that Vatican II had allowed disconnecting tubes in a dying patient. Is that true?

A. Vatican II never even mentioned disconnecting tubes from dying patients, let alone sanctioned this form of euthanasia. As noted in the previous answer, the only time that it would be permissible to stop artificial nutrition and hydration would be if the patient were imminently dying, i.e., the dying process had begun and could not be reversed, and continuing nutrition and hydration would be clearly useless and possibly even burdensome to the patient.

If your aunt were not imminently dying, then withdrawing her food and water was not the least bit humane. It was a cruel option since it causes the patient to die from starvation and dehydration after several days of terrible suffering.

3. Can you give a summary of the pro-life position on artificial nutrition and hydration (ANH)?

A. Here is a summary provided by Msgr. George P. Graham in the May 1999 issue of *Homiletic & Pastoral Review*:

1. First of all, it is gravely immoral directly to destroy an innocent human life.

2. Euthanasia is understood as any action or omission which of itself or by intention causes death, with the purpose of eliminating all suffering. Euthanasia is a grave violation of the law of God.

3. To withhold or withdraw ANH with the intention of bringing about the patient's death is direct killing and is gravely immoral.

4. Even in cases where one may legitimately withdraw technology, such as a ventilator, one may not on the same grounds withdraw ANH.

5. Since the purpose of ANH is not to effect a cure but rather to keep the person alive by providing nutrition, one may not withdraw ANH on the basis that it is ineffective if, in fact, it does keep the patient alive.

6. When ANH would be ineffective, for example, when death is imminent whether the person receives nourishment or not, or when the patient cannot digest food introduced into the stomach or intestines, one may legitimately withhold ANH on the ground that it is ineffective.

Projects:

1. Assign students to review some of the resources mentioned below and report to the class.
2. Bring in to class clippings about artificial nutrition and hydration from newspapers and magazines.
3. Write letters to newspapers and radio and television stations urging respect for the dignity of those with terminal illnesses.
4. Write to lawmakers urging them to sponsor and vote for bills that would protect innocent human life.

References:

John Paul II, Pope. *Evangelium Vitae* ("The Gospel of Life")
McHugh, Bishop James T. *Principles in Regard to
        Withholding Artificial Nutrition and Hydration*
Pontifical Council for Pastoral Assistance. *Charter for
        Health Care Workers*
Sacred Congregation for the Doctrine of the Faith.
        Declaration on Euthanasia
Smith, Wesley J. *Forced Exit*

Hypnosis, Drugs and AIDS

Purpose: The purpose of this lesson is to discuss the ethical principles governing hypnosis, lie detector tests, alcohol and drug addiction, and AIDS.

Tips for Teachers: This lesson covers a potpourri of issues, all related to the preservation of life, that can be discussed individually. The catechist could start with hypnosis, describing what it is and the conditions that must be met before one submits to it. Obviously, there should be a serious reason for undergoing hypnosis and the hypnotist must be properly trained and of good moral character.

As for polygraph tests, we are normally not obliged to take them since neither moral law nor civil law commands us to testify against ourself. However, we might be obliged under the natural law if our refusal would cause grave harm to a third party or to the common good.

The problems of alcohol and drug abuse are well-known. They are a violation of the Fifth Commandment, which obliges us to care for our life and health and those of others. Stress that it is not the legal *use* of these substances that is the problem, but rather the *abuse* of them. Point out the distinction the Bible makes between the use and abuse of alcohol (cf. Proverbs 20:1 and 31:6-7 and Ephesians 5:18 and 1 Timothy 5:23).

You can use the test under "Some Questions and Answers" to help the students determine if they have a problem with alcohol or drugs. They should also ponder the 12 Steps of Alcoholics Anonymous, which can be applied to drug addiction, too.

Finally, we are to preserve our life and health by staying away from promiscuous sexual activities that could expose us to sexually transmitted diseases, including the deadly AIDS virus. Those who urge "safe sex" through condoms are spreading a false and dangerous message, as those who have become pregnant or contracted a sex-related disease, despite condom use, can painfully testify. Practicing chastity and staying away from alcohol and drugs are the only guaranteed ways of avoiding sexually transmitted diseases.

Topics for Discussion:

1. Is hypnosis a harmless activity?
2. Should we submit to lie detector tests if asked to do so?
3. Which of AA's 12 steps is the most important and why?
4. What is the best way to curb the spread of AIDS?
5. What do we mean by saying that we should hate the sin but love the sinner?

Some Questions and Answers:

1. Is there a quiz that I could give to my class to help them decide whether any of them have a problem with alcohol or drugs?
A. Here is one you can use:

— Have I ever said I could stop drinking or taking drugs anytime I wanted to, but then continued abusing them?
— Have I ever decided to stop drinking or taking drugs for a week or two, only to find that my resolve lasted only a day or two?
— Do I get mad when people ask me about my drinking or drug abuse?
— Do I ever drink or take illegal drugs in the morning?
— Do alcohol or drugs ever cause me trouble at home, in school, or on the job?
— Have I missed school or work because of alcohol or drugs?
— Do I sometimes have blackouts or partial loss of memory?
— Have I ever switched from one kind of liquor or drug in the hope that it would keep me from getting drunk or high?
— Have I ever felt that my life would be much better if I stopped drinking or taking drugs?

If any of your students answered yes to one of these questions, he or she may have a problem. If they answered yes to three or more questions, they definitely have a problem. Please steer them to people or agencies who can help them.

2. What do you say to someone who claims that homosexuals and lesbians cannot help the way they are and that they should be free to live according to their inclinations?

A. By that logic, we could say that heavy drinkers, compulsive gamblers, prostitutes, and drug addicts should be able to continue their destructive lifestyles, too, since they really can't help themselves. There is no clear evidence that homosexuals and lesbians are born that way; there is credible evidence that their inclination is the result of defects in the parent-child relationship in the early years of life or of seduction by an adult homosexual. But even if it should ever be established that homosexuals are genetically programmed to act that way, there would be no change in the Church's teaching that everyone, homosexual or heterosexual, is called to lead a chaste life.

For persuasive evidence that homosexuals are not born that way, and that they can either change their inclination and enter into happy heterosexual marriages, or live chastely as homosexuals, see *Homosexuality: The Questions*, by Dr. Joseph Dilenno and Herbert Smith, S.J., or Fr. John Harvey's two books, *The Homosexual Person* and *The Truth About Homosexuality*.

Father Harvey spent more than 30 years counseling homosexuals and founded Courage, an organization that helps homosexually inclined persons to lead chaste lives through spiritual counseling, prayer, and frequent use of the Sacraments.

Projects:

1. Start a club at your school or among your friends to postpone drinking alcohol at least until you are of legal age and, if then, only in moderation.

2. Attend a meeting of Alcoholics Anonymous.

3. Start a club or movement to save sex until marriage.

4. Volunteer to help at a place for those with addictions.

5. Volunteer to help at an AIDS hospice.

6. Organize a prayer service or Eucharistic adoration for those addicted to destructive lifestyles.

References:

Catechism of the Catholic Church
Catholic Almanac
Dilenno, Joseph A., M.D., and Smith, Herbert F., S.J.,
    Homosexuality: The Questions
Drummey, James J. *Catholic Replies*
Grisez, Germain. *Christian Moral Principles*
_____. *Difficult Moral Questions*
_____. *Living a Christian Life*
Hardon, John A., S.J. *The Catholic Catechism*
Harvey, John F., O.S.F.S. *The Homosexual Person*
_____. *The Truth About Homosexuality*
Hayes, Edward J., Hayes, Paul J. and Drummey, James J.
    Catholicism and Life
_____. *Catholicism and Society*
John Paul II, Pope. *Evangelium Vitae* ("The Gospel of Life")
_____. *Veritatis Splendor* ("The Splendor of Truth")
Lawler, Ronald, Boyle, Joseph and May, William E. *Catholic
    Sexual Ethics*
Sacred Congregation for the Doctrine of the Faith.
    Declaration on Certain Problems of Sexual Ethics
_____. *Letter to Bishops of the Catholic Church on the
    Pastoral Care of Homosexual Persons*
Thayer, Linda. *AIDS & Adolescents*
Wuerl, Donald, Lawler, Thomas and Lawler, Ronald. *The
    Catholic Catechism*
_____. *The Teaching of Christ*

Spiritual Help for the Suffering

Purpose: The purpose of this lesson is to explain the Catholic position on suffering and to encourage those who are called to suffer to unite their suffering with that of Jesus on the cross.

Tips for Teachers: Suffering has always been a great mystery, so don't expect your class to grasp in one lesson what has eluded many brilliant thinkers over the centuries. Another obstacle in presenting the Christian perspective on suffering is the attitude of the worldly, who think that no one should experience pain or anxiety and that all suffering is a waste.

All the catechist can hope to do is give the students some understanding of what suffering is all about. The material in Pope John Paul's apostolic letter on suffering, *Salvifici Doloris*, and in Peter Kreeft's book *Making Sense Out of Suffering* will help in preparing and teaching this lesson.

Start by getting the students' thoughts on such common questions as "Why does God permit people to suffer?" Or "Why do bad things happen to good people?" Or "Can one expect to go through life without experiencing any suffering?"

Once the class has had a chance to express its views on these and similar questions, recall for the students the suffering Jesus himself experienced during his Passion and death. Remind them that the symbol of our Faith is the cross, not the reclining chair. Chapter 7 of *Catholicism and Reason*, a companion text in this series, offers a wonderful summary and meditation on what Jesus suffered for us and for our sins. Or the teacher could assign reading the accounts of the Passion in each of the four Gospels.

Ask why they think Jesus chose such a horrible way to die. Why didn't he take an easier way? Explain that he wanted to show us the horror of sin and also to set an example for us to follow. We can't say, "Jesus doesn't know what it's like to be abandoned by all your friends." Or "Jesus doesn't know what it's like to suffer." Or "Jesus doesn't know what it's like to be ridiculed or persecuted or falsely accused of something."

The fact is, Jesus knows exactly what all these things mean, and he will help us cope with our personal crosses. The catechist might ask at this point what some of the crosses are that people have to bear. There are plenty of examples.

Another point to make is that hard work is required to accomplish anything worthwhile (ask for examples), whether it's sports, the honor roll, a promotion at work, etc. The same is true of getting to heaven. But as St. Paul said: "I consider the sufferings of the present to be as nothing compared to the glory to be revealed in us" (Romans 8:17-18).

Ask the class what the glory of heaven might be like. Some interesting insights can be gained in Peter Kreeft's book *Everything You Ever Wanted to Know About Heaven.*

Emphasize the point that when crosses come into our life, we shouldn't whine and complain or ask, "Why me?" Rather, we should say, "Thy will be done," and ask the Lord for help in carrying our crosses, bearing in mind that the sorrow of every Good Friday is followed by the joy of an Easter Sunday.

Go over the insights into evil and suffering on pages 182-183 of the text. You could even review the Genesis account of the fall of Adam and Eve, which led to our present state of affairs. However, just as God brought good out of that evil through the Incarnation and Jesus' subsequent death on the cross, so he can also bring good out of the suffering in today's world. See Pope John Paul's comments on pages 183-184 of the text for some thoughts on how to cope with suffering.

Lastly, have the class familiarize itself with the prayers for the sick and dying on pages 189-193 of the text.

Topics for Discussion:

1. Why is there evil and suffering in the world?

2. Why do bad things seem to happen to good people?

3. Couldn't Jesus have saved us in a less painful and bloody manner?

4. What are some crosses people have to carry in this life?

5. Can you think of some good that can come about from suffering?

6. What joys will we experience in heaven that will more than make up for the pains of this life?

Projects:

1. Read a Gospel account of Jesus' suffering and death, or read the summary of the four Gospel accounts that appears in chapter 7 of *Catholicism and Reason*. Or read Dr. Pierre Barbet's medical account of the crucifixion in *A Doctor at Calvary*.

2. Read about the early Christian martyrs who died for their Catholic Faith and report to the class on their lives. St. Stephen is one example (cf. Acts of the Apostles, chapters 6 and 7).

3. Read the lives of modern-day martyrs for Christ, such as Maximilian Kolbe and Edith Stein, both of whom died in Nazi concentration camps during World War II, and tell their stories to the class.

4. Volunteer at a hospital, hospice, nursing home, or other health-care facility.

5. Arrange a prayer service using some of the prayers on pages 189-193 of the text.

References:

Catechism of the Catholic Church
Barbet, Pierre. *A Doctor at Calvary*
Grisez, Germain. *Christian Moral Principles*
_____. *Difficult Moral Questions*
_____. *Living a Christian Life*
Hardon, John A., S.J. *The Catholic Catechism*
Hayes, Edward J., Hayes, Paul J. and Drummey, James J.
      Catholicism and Reason
John Paul II, Pope. *Salvifici Doloris* ("On the Christian
      Meaning of Suffering")
Kreeft, Peter. *Everything You Ever Wanted to Know About
      Heaven*
_____. *Making Sense Out of Suffering*